THE WONDER OF
Light

THE WONDER OF
Light

A PICTURE STORY OF
HOW AND WHY WE SEE

BY Hy Ruchlis

DRAWINGS BY
Alice Hirsh

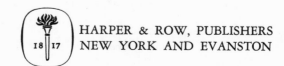

HARPER & ROW, PUBLISHERS
NEW YORK AND EVANSTON

THE WONDER OF LIGHT: A Picture Story of How and Why We See

Copyright © 1960 by Hyman Ruchlis
Printed in the United States of America

Library of Congress catalog card number: 59-8977

Contents

PART I

How Light Behaves

1 Light Energy

WHAT would the world be like if there were no light?

There would be no trees or other plants on the earth because plants need light to make them grow. Thus there would be no food and no one could live on the earth.

There would be no air and no wind. Without the warmth provided by light from the sun the air would freeze and fall as "liquid air." The water on the earth would freeze. Winds would stop blowing. Rivers would stop flowing.

There would be no soil because soil is formed by the gradual wearing down of rock by wind, rain, and the chemical action of air and living things. The continents would be covered by nothing but bare rocks, ice, and liquid or solid air.

So you see that without light our earth would be a completely dead planet.

Fortunately, the sun keeps shining and shedding its light. The earth stays warm enough to keep man alive. The water evaporates. The air remains a gas. The heat caused by light starts the giant cycle of winds and rains that water the earth and set the conditions for life in the ocean and on the continents.

THE SPEED OF LIGHT

We say that we can "see" light. But do we? As we shall find out later in the book, our eyes merely detect the presence of light and form an image of lights and darks. From these images we learn to recognize things. But we do not see what light itself is.

The key to the nature of light is provided by the things that light can *do*. Since it causes heat, moves the winds, and makes plants grow, light must be some kind of *energy* closely connected with *motion*.

An important clue was uncovered in the seventeenth century when telescopes revealed that Jupiter had at least four moons. One of these moons is shown in Fig. 1. As astronomers watched the moons revolve about Jupiter, they noticed that each moon had a definite period or time of revolution around the planet. In a similar way our moon revolves about the earth in a definite time. But there was a most peculiar thing about the revolutions of the moons of Jupiter. They seemed to revolve a bit faster as the earth approached Jupiter and to slow down as the earth moved away from the planet. For a half year, as the earth moved closer to Jupiter, the moons would speed up. For the next half year, as the earth moved away, the moons revolved more slowly.

In 1676, the Dutch scientist Olaus Roemer offered

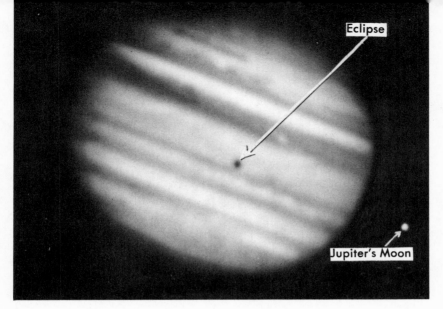

Fig. 1. The moons of Jupiter provided the first clue that light had a definite speed. (Mount Wilson and Palomar Observatories)

a startling explanation for this curious fact. He thought that light traveled at a certain speed and therefore required time to cross the vast distance between Jupiter and the earth. When the earth was farthest away from Jupiter, as in Fig. 2, the light arriving at the earth from Jupiter required an extra fifteen minutes to cross the additional distance.

Roemer made some calculations. Knowing the distance across the earth's orbit and the time required for the light to cross it, he was able to calculate the

Fig. 2. The rotation of Jupiter's moon seems fifteen minutes behind schedule at point A because of the time needed for light to cross the extra distance across the earth's orbit.

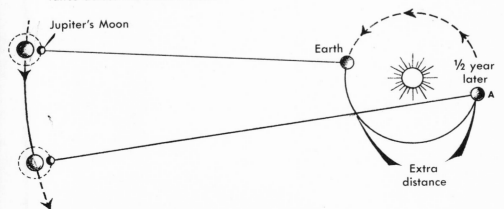

speed of light. His answer was quite close to the figure of *186,000 miles a second,* which we accept to-day as the speed of light.

Stop a minute. Think about that fantastic speed. How can anything go that fast? At such a speed light can go round and round the earth about seven times in a second! *It could go once around the earth in the time you wink your eye.*

But are we sure this is so?

Since Roemer, other methods have been used to measure the speed of light. A number of scientists have timed the passage of a beam of light as it passed between two places on earth. The most famous of these experiments was performed in 1902 by the American scientist Albert Michelson. He accurately timed a light beam as it traveled from one mountaintop to another, then bounced off a mirror and returned to the starting point (Fig. 3). The forty-four-mile distance was covered in less than a thousandth of a second. Michelson's measurements were so accurate that he was able to express the speed of light as 186,265 miles per second with an error of probably not than a few miles per second.

THE PUSH OF A LIGHT BEAM

We can learn much about light from astronomy. Comets tell an interesting story. You have seen photographs of comets with long, streaming tails. What causes these tails?

Comets travel in curved orbits around the sun

6

(Fig. 4). When they are far away from the sun, their streaming tails are not particularly long. But as they approach the sun, the tails enlarge and may stretch out for a million miles or more. The tails always stream in a direction away from the sun. As a comet reaches the part of its orbit nearest the sun, a strange thing happens. The comet begins to move away from the sun tail first!

This seems to contradict our experience on earth, where objects with long taillike streamers do not move tail first. But the rules that apply on earth don't necessarily apply out in space. Streamers tag behind in our atmosphere because of air resistance. As air is pushed out of the way by a moving object, it grabs and drags the fluffier or spread-out parts of the object. But there is no air out in space to cause a comet's tail to drag along behind the head.

The comet has a tail because "something" coming from the sun pushes the gases in the comet. It is thought that in some cases the push comes from light, and in other cases from high-speed particles. As the comet approaches the sun and then begins to move away, sunlight and high-speed particles push

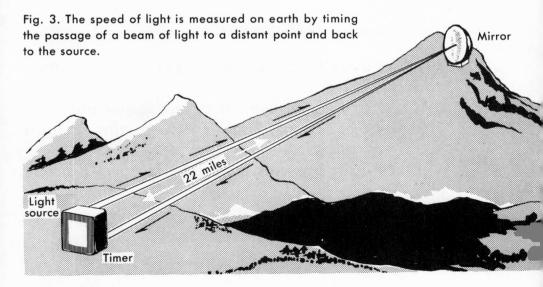

Fig. 3. The speed of light is measured on earth by timing the passage of a beam of light to a distant point and back to the source.

Mirror

22 miles

Light source

Timer

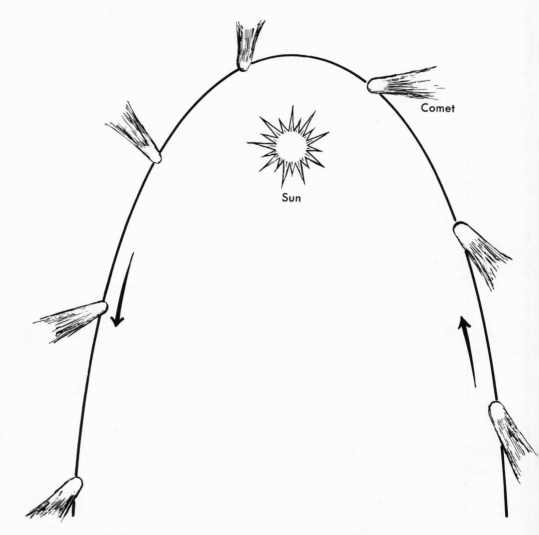

Fig. 4. The pressure of the sun's light causes comets to recede tail first.

its gases away from the sun, thus causing the comet to move tail first.

This tail-first movement of the comet indicates that light has energy; that it is in motion at high speed and can exert force.

Does light push us on earth? It does. But the

push is so slight that it can be measured only with very delicate instruments.

CHANGES CAUSED BY LIGHT

There are other things which show that light is connected with motion and has energy (the ability to cause changes). Light causes electric currents in our eyeballs that race up the nerves to our brains. We then interpret these electric-current messages to see things.

We have already mentioned that light produces heat. Solar heating is a practical use of this fact. In some experimental "solar-heated houses" very large windows capture enough light energy to keep the houses heated all winter without any fuel. Special chemicals store heat for times when the sun is not shining.

Have you ever watched a photographer use a "light meter" to measure the amount of light before he takes a picture? He points the meter at the scene and the motion of a pointer records the amount of light present. The operation of the meter is quite simple. Light striking a special material in the meter causes it to generate electricity to move the pointer. This effect is called *photoelectricity.*

Scientists are now experimenting with materials that will produce larger amounts of electricity when they are illuminated. They have developed "solar batteries" which can operate telephone systems using nothing but power from sunlight. Similar solar batteries power radio transmitters and other equipment used in earth satellites.

Television would not be possible without the ability of light to make electric current. At the studio the TV camera produces an image on a screen which then changes the patterns of lights and darks into electric-current patterns. The current is then amplified (magnified), mixed with other electric signals, and sent out as radio (TV) waves. In your TV set the signals are unscrambled and magnified to produce the image on the screen. Such rapid changes are possible only because light is a form of energy.

Photographic film records an image because light affects chemicals. It changes the material on the film sufficiently so that we can develop a complete picture of the places where the light struck.

You have probably noticed that some storekeepers cover their windows with large sheets of yellow plastic. This is done to preserve the colors in the materials being displayed. Light can change chemicals in dyes and thus alter colors. Similarly, a housewife will close the blinds in a sunny room to prevent sunlight from fading the colors of the fabrics on her furniture.

All of the changes caused by light show that it is a form of energy.

LIGHT AND RELATIVITY

The speed of light plays an important part in Albert Einstein's Theory of Relativity.

Let us imagine that a space ship is being pushed faster and faster by its rocket motor. The Theory of Relativity states that as an object gains in speed it also gains in mass (or heaviness). That is to say, the faster a space ship travels, the more massive (heavier) it becomes. And the more massive the ship becomes, the harder it is to increase its speed. As the ship approaches the speed of light, its mass increases very rapidly. When it finally reaches the speed of light, the ship will be so massive that it cannot be made to go any faster, no matter how great a push is supplied. Thus, according to Einstein's theory nothing can go faster than the speed of light—186,265 miles per second.

Scientists have gathered a great deal of evidence to show that these ideas are correct. There is little doubt today that light is something very basic in our universe and is closely connected with motions of ordinary objects.

Another clue to the important part played by light in our universe is found in Einstein's famous formula $E = MC^2$. The E stands for *energy,* M for mass (roughly equivalent to weight), and C for a fundamental "constant" in the universe, the *speed of light.* The small 2 above the C means that the speed of light (C) must be multiplied by itself (squared). If a scientist wants to find out how much nuclear (atomic) energy would be released by destroying a certain amount of matter, this formula enables him to make the calculation.

You can see that by multiplying the mass by the speed of light, and then again by the speed of light, you would get an enormous figure for the amount of energy.

What happens inside nuclear reactors, or when A-bombs and H-bombs are set off, is that matter is destroyed and changed into tremendous quantities of energy.

It is difficult to see at first how light can be connected with matter. But scientists are beginning to think that atoms of matter may be made up of waves similar to light, and that it is the motion of these waves that gives rise to particles of matter.

If these ideas seem strange, remember that we have only five senses with which to find out about the world around us. When we feel a stone, we can tell whether it is rough or smooth. But we don't get any idea of the motions and commotions of the atoms in the stone. When we look at a person, we get some idea as to his shape, size, and color. But we don't see, feel, or hear what makes him a live person. So we mustn't be surprised when we are told that the seemingly solid matter in our world may be closer in nature to light than it is to the things we consider solid.

We have seen that light is a form of energy and is therefore connected with motion. But motion of what? Before we can answer this question it will be necessary to find out more about the way in which light behaves.

2 Seeing Things

WE can learn a good deal about light by studying the magician's trick in Fig. 5. To the audience the girl appears suspended in mid-air, without any support. To "prove" this, the magician passes a hoop around her body.

The magician has set up his trick by making use of certain facts about light. You know that some source of light is needed in order to see an object. But the light from that object must also reach your eye, otherwise you can't see it.

The magician uses a very intense source of light from a spotlight offstage. Light moves out from the spotlight and strikes the magician, the girl, and the black curtain behind her.

Only if light *reflects* (bounces off) does it reach your eye. Black objects appear black or dark because they *absorb* most of the light and reflect very little. White objects appear bright because they reflect most of the light and absorb very little. Practically no light reaches the audience from the black curtain behind the magician. Therefore, they do not see it. The stand and board supporting the girl are

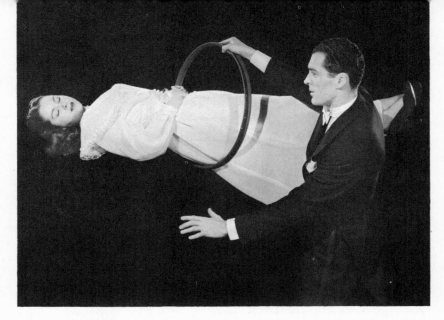

Fig. 5. The magician bases his trick upon the fact that black objects do not reflect light and therefore cannot be seen against a black background. (Ewing Galloway)

painted jet black to make them invisible against the equally black curtain.

You may wonder how the magician passes the hoop around the stand. The sections of the stand are probably hinged so that they can open up to permit the hoop to pass by. For example, suppose that four black steel rods held up the board upon which the girl rests. An assistant could easily manipulate a lever behind the curtain to lower each rod as the hoop went by. The three remaining rods would still be able to support the board.

Notice that although the magician's suit is black, it is slightly visible. There are many degrees of blackness and whiteness. An object is as white as it can possibly be if it reflects every bit of the light that strikes it. If it reflects nine-tenths of the light, it is still considered white. If it reflects one-half, it is

14

gray; if it reflects one-tenth, it is dark black. If it reflects no light at all and absorbs all the light that reaches it, it is perfectly black.

Can a white object appear black? Yes—if you look at a white object in complete darkness, it looks just as black as everything else. In the absence of a source of light, there is no light for the object to reflect. In total darkness everything looks black.

Notice that the brightest part of Fig. 6 is the top of the airplane. This is easy to understand when we remember that the source of illumination, the sun, is overhead. When the picture was taken, light striking the top of the airplane was reflected to the camera to produce an intense white area on the film.

Fig. 6. Reflection of the sun's light makes the top of the airplane and the ground visible. The shadow is caused by the way in which the airplane blocks light from the sun. (North American Aviation)

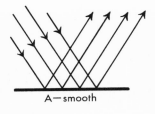
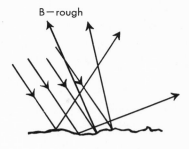

Fig. 7. Smooth surfaces produce mirrorlike reflections. Rough surfaces cause diffused reflections.

The earth below the airplane is also white. But why isn't it as bright as the top of the airplane?

There are two reasons. First, the smoothness or roughness of a surface affects its ability to reflect light. When a beam of light is reflected from a smooth surface, it keeps its shape (Fig. 7A). When light is reflected from a rough surface, the rays are *diffused,* that is, scattered and spread out (Fig. 7B). The body of the airplane is smooth and causes a shining, mirrorlike reflection that concentrates the light from certain parts of the airplane. The plastic dome just above the pilot gives a similar reflection.

Because of the diffuse reflection from the rough ground (Fig. 7B), the light reaches our eyes evenly from all parts, and we see a large grayish area without very bright spots.

The second reason for the greater whiteness of the top of the airplane is the fact that its smooth metal surface reflects a higher percentage of the light than the ground.

Why is the shadow of the airplane so black? No light from the sun passes through the airplane. An object that lets no light pass through is said to be

16

opaque. Since the ground directly underneath the airplane receives no light at all, we see a black *shadow.*

A similar shadow is seen in Fig. 1. Jupiter's moon is opaque and blocks the sun's rays to form an eclipse—a dark shadow on the planet's surface. When our moon passes between the sun and the earth, it causes a similar eclipse on earth.

Now compare the underside of the airplane in Fig. 6 with its shadow on the ground. Since the bottom of the airplane is also blocked from the sun's rays, why does it appear to be gray? Why isn't it as black as its shadow?

We have seen that light is diffusely reflected upward from the rough ground in all directions. Some of this diffused light illuminates the airplane from below and makes it dimly visible. Additional light comes from particles of dust in the air which scatter the sun's light and soften the deep shadows. If some light did not come from the sky and the surroundings in this manner, all shadows would be jet black. The sky would also be jet black and the stars would be visible in the daytime!

Notice that the pilot in Fig. 6 can be seen clearly through the solid plastic dome. The plastic is *transparent* and permits the pilot to receive light from outside while the solidity of the material protects him from the wind.

Look at the shiny spot at the top of the plastic dome. Although most of the light is *transmitted* (passes) through the transparent plastic, a small percentage is reflected. Since the plastic is smooth, you see reflections only at certain angles. One area of the plastic surface was in the proper position to reflect light from the sun to the camera. It appears as a shiny bright spot in the photograph.

Why do we see the markings on the airplane? The markings are visible only because they reflect a different percentage of light than the body of the airplane. That is why we use dark paint on a white or silvery surface, and white paint on a dark surface. We print black ink on a white page and paint white letters on a black background. White paint would be barely visible on the shiny metal surface because both the paint and the metal would reflect a great deal of light, making it hard to tell one from the other.

Why is the shadow of the airplane so clear and sharp? Why does it have a shape similar to that of the airplane?

The straight beams in Fig. 8 show that *light tends to travel in straight lines.* You sometimes see similar straight beams of light when a distant cloud passes between you and the sun.

When sunlight streaming from the sun strikes the airplane in Fig. 6 none of it gets through. It is either *absorbed* (taken in) by the airplane or reflected. But the light grazing the edge of the airplane passes straight on to reach the ground. That is why there is a rather sharp boundary line between the shadow on the ground under the airplane and the rest of the ground, which is illuminated by sunlight. The shape of the shadow on the ground thus follows the curves of the airplane above it.

Fig. 8. Searchlight beams travel in straight lines. (Westinghouse Photo)

If the light beams in Fig. 8 travel in straight lines, why do you see them? Shouldn't the light travel straight off into space without reaching your eye (or the camera)?

Dust and water droplets in the atmosphere cause reflection of light to our eyes. We see light beams because some reflected light reaches our eyes from particles along the straight path of the light.

Because of the great distance of the beam in Fig. 8, we can't see the individual dust particles. Instead, we see the regions from which the billions of particles reflect light. However, if you closely examine a beam of sunlight in your room, you will see some of the individual bits of dust.

19

There are times when light does not travel in a straight line. For example, as light strikes an object, the direction of the beam is sharply changed by reflection. In Chapter 5 we shall see that a change in direction also occurs at the moment a light beam passes from one transparent material into another, such as from air into water.

Why does the sky appear black in Fig. 8? The lights from the city streets are too weak to illuminate the dust particles in the air above the city and lighten the sky. Compare the intense light we receive from the sun—93 million miles away—with the feeble electric lamps that only illuminate objects in their vicinity. Both the sun and the lamps are *luminous,* but there is a vast difference in the amount of light they give.

In Fig. 9 the illumination in the girl's mouth is caused by light beams from the two flashlights. Some of this light passes right through her cheeks. The cheeks are said to be *translucent.* A ground-glass

Fig. 9. Light can penetrate flesh. (Black Star)

window and a piece of waxed paper are also translucent. This means that light goes through, but the direction of the rays is changed from a straight-line path. As a result you cannot see objects when you look through translucent glass. But you can see the light which gets through.

Light passes through *transparent* glass, such as a windowpane, practically without any change of direction. It is almost as though the glass were not there. That is why you can see through a solid glass window.

Light can penetrate every material that is thin enough. But whether we consider a material opaque, transparent, or translucent depends on how much light gets through. If a large percentage of the light penetrates a material without changing the direction of its rays, that material is said to be transparent. If the percentage of light coming through is very small, the material is opaque. If a high percentage of light gets through, but most of the rays are deflected from a straight path, the material is translucent.

Clear water only a few feet deep is transparent. But if you go down 1000 feet in the ocean, so little light comes through that the water might be considered opaque. Some light might pass through a metal film a fraction of a millionth of an inch thick, but a sheet of metal one-thousandth of an inch will stop practically all the light.

Air is usually considered transparent. But if you look at a distant scene, through many miles of air even on a clear day, the dust particles scatter the light waves so that little light comes straight through. See how hazy the background appears in Fig. 10. The road and the trees gradually fade away until there is nothing but a general whiteness. At this point the air can be said to be translucent. Fig. 11 shows a similar occurrence in outer space. Photographed through the telescope, the "Horsehead" Nebula seems to be a large dense cloud surrounded by a luminous cloud of gas. Astronomers tell us that the seemingly dense cloud is made up of gas, far more rarefied (thinner) than that of our atmosphere. But although the gas is very thin, the cloud is many millions of miles thick. Thus, while one mile of the gas absorbs only a tiny fraction of light, many millions of miles absorb most of the light. Such a small percentage of light passes through the cloud that we may consider it opaque.

Fig. 10. Dust and water particles in the air make it difficult to see distant objects clearly. (Hiller Helicopters)

Fig. 11. Opaque dust clouds in outer space block light from distant stars. (Mount Wilson and Palomar Observatories)

We seem to see a few stars through the black area of the cloud. These stars are probably closer to us than the cloud. Notice that more stars are seen in the lighter regions at the left of the picture than in the darker portions to the right. This is probably because the opaque cloud blocks off our view of most, if not all, of the stars behind it. Since the luminous part of the cloud is more rarefied, it allows us to see many stars beyond it. We also see this part of the dust cloud because of reflections from particles of dust.

SCREEN PROBLEM

Fig. 12 is a photograph of a corner of a screened porch. An interesting pattern of dark whirls is seen through the screen. The pattern appears only when you look through two layers of screening. Try to figure out why the pattern occurs. Then turn to page 149 and compare the answer with yours.

Fig. 12. What causes the wavy dark and light areas you see when you look through two porch screens?

3 Illumination

IN Fig. 13 two men seem to be diving into a pool, one above the other. Actually the photograph is a "double exposure" of the same diver. Two pictures were taken in rapid succession on the same negative with the camera in the same position.

How can you tell? Look closely at the diver entering the water. Notice that a faint image of one post and tiles appears right through his body. This means that the picture was taken twice: once when the diver was high in the air and again as he hit the water. The first photograph showed the diver above the diving board and included a complete picture of the posts and tiles on the side of the pool. When the second photo was snapped, the image of the tiles and posts was already recorded on the film. Thus both the diver and the objects behind him are in the same place on the film.

Why does the diver appear much more brightly illuminated than the side of the pool? And if we look at the top of the photograph, we do not see any image of the ceiling through the diver as he leaves the diving board. We would expect such an

25

Fig. 13. The background objects receive less illumination than the diver because they are farther from the source of light. (Dr. Harold E. Edgerton)

image to appear when the second picture was snapped.

It is all a matter of *illumination*—the amount of light that falls on a surface. Notice the difference in the brightness of the face of the clock to the left of the pool and the skin of the diver. Although the clock face is certainly as white, or whiter, than the diver's skin, it does not appear that way in the picture. If you look closely under the diving board, you will see a faint image of a man watching the dive. The white clock appears gray, and the onlooker's image is rather dim because they are at a greater distance from the source of illumination than the diver.

Why should distance have such an effect on illumination?

Throw a stone into a quiet pool of water. A wave spreads out. As it does, the disturbance that began at the center of the wave moves outward in a wider and wider circle. As it spreads, the "hill" of water becomes lower and lower, until it just seems to die out and disappear at a distance. In many ways light acts like a water wave.

Hold a book near the light from a lamp. The page appears bright and is easy to read. But move the book away from the lamp and the page becomes dimmer and dimmer until finally the print can be barely seen.

Illumination depends mainly upon two conditions: the strength of the light source and the distance from the source.

Lamps are rated in *candlepower*. A certain type of candle is taken as "one candlepower." A lamp that produces ten times as much light is rated as ten candlepower. We can increase illumination by increasing the brightness (candlepower) of the source of light.

How does distance affect illumination? Fig. 14 shows a light beam traveling outward from a lamp at L. A square screen marked A is placed one foot away from the lamp. Light from the lamp (L) covers the screen and provides a certain amount of illumination.

Let us now remove screen A and allow the light to fall on screen B, two feet from L. As a light beam travels from its source, it spreads out. It is twice as high and twice as wide when it strikes B as it was when it illuminated screen A, yet B receives exactly the same amount of light energy that illuminated screen A. Since the light energy that formerly covered one square now covers four, each of the four squares on B receives one-fourth as much light.

Square C is three times as far from the lamp and is three times as high and as wide as square A. It captures the same total amount of light energy as A. But it consists of nine squares, each the size of screen A. Each of the nine squares in C captures one-ninth of the total light energy, and therefore has one-ninth the illumination of A.

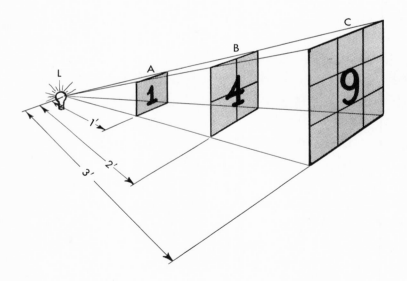

Fig. 14. Illumination decreases rapidly with distance.

Let us now see what happens if we increase the distance.

28

Distance	Illumination Compared to First Distance (A)		
1	1		1
2	$\dfrac{1}{2 \times 2}$	or	$\dfrac{1}{4}$
3	$\dfrac{1}{3 \times 3}$	or	$\dfrac{1}{9}$
4	$\dfrac{1}{4 \times 4}$	or	$\dfrac{1}{16}$
5	$\dfrac{1}{5 \times 5}$	or	$\dfrac{1}{25}$
10	$\dfrac{1}{10 \times 10}$	or	$\dfrac{1}{100}$
100	$\dfrac{1}{100 \times 100}$	or	$\dfrac{1}{10,000}$
1000	$\dfrac{1}{1000 \times 1000}$	or	$\dfrac{1}{1,000,000}$

You can see from the table that the illumination rapidly decreases as we go farther from the light source. Very soon the illumination drops to practically nothing.

The rapid reduction in illumination with increased distance explains why the image of the diver in Fig. 13 is clearly recorded by the camera while the on-looker behind him is almost invisible. Measure the length of the diver's body from head to toe. Now measure the figure of the onlooker. The diver's body is about twice as long. This means that the onlooker is twice as far from the camera as the diver. Illumination from the camera's flash lamp is therefore four times as great for the diver as for the onlooker.

It might seem that with one-fourth the illumination the onlooker would not appear as faint as he does in the picture. But we must remember that photographic film does not record illumination in the same way as our eyes. In photographs, dimly lit areas generally reproduce darker than they appear to the eye.

ILLUMINATION FROM THE SUN

We take so many things for granted. For example, a certain "angle" has a very important effect on your life. It determines whether you are warm or cold, whether you prefer to live at the North Pole or the equator, whether you wear a heavy coat or just a bathing suit.

It is the angle at which the sun's rays strike the earth that determines which parts of the earth are cold or warm, and when and where summer or winter occurs.

What causes summer and winter?

Some people think that we have winter when the earth is farthest from the sun, and summer when the earth is closest to the sun. This cannot be so because it is winter in the Northern Hemisphere when it is summer in the Southern Hemisphere, and both hemispheres are always practically the same distance from the sun. If distance from the sun were the cause of winter and summer, the two hemispheres would have the same seasons at the same time.

Fig. 15 provides a clue. Notice the long shadow of the camel on the curved sand dune, near the arrow. Why does the sand appear gray at this slop-

Fig. 15. The sloping angle at which rays of sunlight strike the sand dune causes reduced illumination on the ground. (American Museum of Natural History)

ing point, rather than white? It cannot be caused by a shadow, since the shadows of the camels are clearly seen on the sand on either side of the gray area.

The part of the sand dune that slopes away from the sun causes the light energy to spread out over a much larger surface. Thus each square inch of ground along the slope gets less light energy and appears less bright. In effect, the illumination is less.

The same effect is shown in Fig. 16. The light from beam 2 strikes the earth "directly" at B. Notice that beam 2 covers much less surface of the earth than the equal beams 1 and 3, which strike the earth at a glancing angle nearer to the poles. The large areas, A and C, receive the same amount of light energy as the smaller area B, which is nearer to the equator. But the light energy is more concentrated at B, and it spreads out at A and C. Since light energy causes the heating of the earth, region B is warmer than A or C.

In Fig. 16 the earth's axis is shown with its North Pole tilted at an angle toward the sun. This is the position for summer in the Northern Hemisphere and winter in the Southern. Region B, a bit north of the equator, gets the greatest concentration of light. The North Pole region at A gets as much light energy as region C in the southern temperate zone, and the region of the South Pole is in complete darkness.

The extremes of climate on earth are therefore caused by the changes in the intensity of sunlight, owing mainly to the angle at which the light happens to hit the surface of our round earth.

Fig. 16. The polar regions are cold because the glancing angle of the sun's rays reduces illumination from the sun.

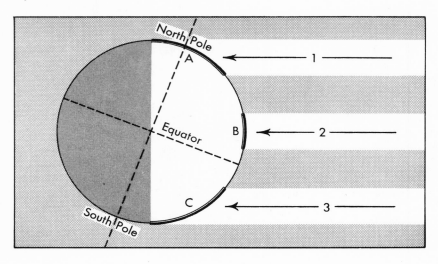

4 Mirrors

THE painters on the scaffold in Fig. 17 would be surprised to learn that we plan to use them to illustrate some principles of light.

Look closely at the image of the scaffold and painters in the windows. We are quite certain that the windows are made of transparent glass. Yet we can't see through them into the building. Why not? And why is the mirror image in the window so dim?

Any very smooth surface produces a mirror image. For example, the water is smooth in front of the boat in Fig. 18 and rough behind it. We see a mirror image of the boat in the smooth water, and the water itself seems invisible. A polished table, a shiny car, a new spoon, and other smooth surfaces produce similar mirror images. But the mirror image disappears in the roughened water behind the boat. The rough water now appears as a white material. It is white because it reflects light. Yet the type of reflection is very different from that produced by the smooth water. The white appearance of the roughened water is caused by light that is reflected dif-

Fig. 17. Smooth glass produces dim mirror reflections. (Ewing Galloway)

fusely in all directions. We have seen this type of reflection in Fig. 7.

Why do the windows in Fig. 17 produce a mirror image of the painters? Ordinary window glass always produces a mirror image. But why is this image so noticeable? We do not usually see such good reflections in windows.

Notice the line of sunlight on the top window ledge at A above the painters. The photographer snapped the picture at a moment when the sunlight illuminated the painters and yet did not enter the windows. It is therefore very dark behind the windows. But it is very light out-of-doors. Some of the light striking the painters reflects to the window.

But most of the light goes through the window to the inside of the building—and never reaches our eyes or the camera. A small part of the light is reflected from the glass, reaches the camera, and produces the mirror image. The image of the painters is dim because only a small portion of the sunlight reflected from the painters to the window is then reflected back from the window to our eyes. Thus the reflected image of the painters is dimmer than the original appearance of the painters.

But why do ordinary mirrors reflect more light than glass? And why are most mirrors made of glass?

Certain metals, such as silver, aluminum, and stainless steel, reflect most of the light that strikes

Fig. 18. Smooth water produces mirror reflections; rough water reflects light diffusely and appears white. (Century Boat Co.)

them. When flat sheets of these metals are polished, they become excellent mirrors (Fig. 19). Some mirrors are made in this way.

However, thin, flat sheets of metal can be bent easily. Bending distorts the shape of the image, as you can see by studying the reflection in Fig. 19.

It is easy to make flat sheets of glass that are rigid and keep their shape. But glass reflects only a small portion of the light, while permitting most of it to pass through. We then combine the advantages of

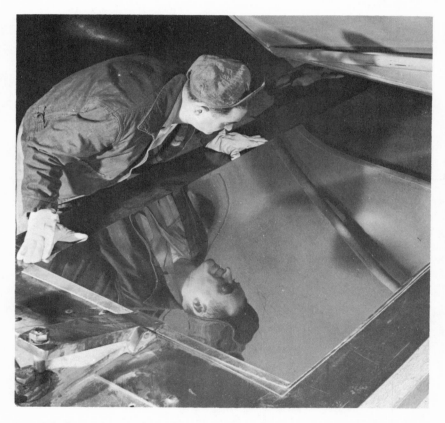

Fig. 19. Smooth metal produces mirror reflections. (United States Steel Corp.)

glass and metal by coating the glass with a thin layer of silver, aluminum, or other metal. The glass provides the flat surface, while the metal coating does most of the reflecting.

Other metals, such as lead and copper, can also be used for mirrors. Since they do not reflect as much light as silver and aluminum, images do not appear as bright. These metals are used in rear-view mirrors in automobiles because they reduce the glare from headlights of other cars.

Many houses are equipped with special peepholes that are covered with a strange kind of glass. When someone outside tries to look in, he can't see inside. He sees only his mirror reflection in the peephole. But the person in the house can see outside with no trouble at all. How can the same material act as a window and as a mirror at the same time?

The girl in Fig. 20 can obviously see through her sunglasses, or she wouldn't be wearing them. Yet the photographer looking into her glasses did not see her eyes. He saw a mirror reflection of himself.

Look again at the painters on the scaffold in Fig. 17. As we look through the window into the darkened interior of the building, we see only a reflection of the bright objects outside. On the other hand, people inside the building could easily see objects outside.

This is caused by the different degrees of brightness on the two sides of the glass. The sunglasses in Fig. 20 are dark and let through only a fraction of the light. They shield the girl's eyes from the strong sunlight. This also means that there is little illumination on her eyes. Only a part of the reduced amount of light reaching her eyes is reflected back. If we are to see her eyes, the light must then pass through the dark glasses. The amount of light that reaches us from the girl's eyes is greatly weakened by this triple reduction and is therefore very faint.

The light that is reflected from the smooth surface of the sunglasses is also reduced in brightness, but only once. The reflected image of the photographer can therefore be seen, while the girl's eyes are invisible.

In the same way a person inside a darkened house looks out through his darkened peephole window to see a person in strong daylight. The person outside, illuminated by bright light, gets a strong reflection of himself; therefore, he cannot see the person in the dim interior.

At night the situation is reversed. The illumination is stronger inside the house and much less outside. Thus the person outside is able to see into the building, while the person inside sees a reflection of himself.

This effect is increased by using glass that is "half silvered." A very thin coating of metal is put onto the glass so that some light gets through and some is reflected. There is then a greater difference between the brightness of the reflected image and the image that we see through the glass.

A similar effect is observed in store windows. At night you can clearly see the interior of a brightly lighted store and your reflected image is usually not visible. But in the daytime, especially when you are

Fig. 20. Why do you see a mirror reflection in the glasses while the girl's eyes cannot be seen? (Wide World)

illuminated by the sun, you see a mirror image of yourself against the darkened store window.

EXPLAINING MIRROR IMAGES

Let us examine Fig. 17 more closely. Notice that the image of the painters and of the scaffold seems to be the same size as the painters and the scaffold. And it appears to be the same distance behind the window as they are in front of the window.

The image seems to be the same as the object, except for one thing — the image is reversed. For example, the painter on the left has his right arm raised. But the image has its left arm raised.

An image in a flat mirror is *symmetrical* with the object reflected. This means that everything on one side of the mirror repeats everything on the other side of the mirror, with the two sides reversed.

We can explain mirror images by observing the way in which light is reflected from a mirror. To study mirror reflection, cut a small hole in a piece of cardboard and allow some light from a flashlight to pass through the hole. This creates a narrow beam of light called a *ray*.

In Fig. 21A a ray of light falls on a mirror and is reflected. Notice that there is an angle between the incoming ray and the mirror (angle 1). There is also an angle between the reflected ray and the mirror (angle 2). The two angles are equal. They demonstrate the *law of reflection,* which (in simplified form) states that the angle at which a ray of light reflects from a surface is equal to the angle at which it strikes the surface.

Fig. 21B shows the incoming ray striking the mirror at a different angle. Again the reflected ray also bounces off at the same angle at which it strikes the mirror.

In Fig. 22 a beam of light is reflected eleven times from a series of mirrors inside a device that "chops" a light beam into rapid pulses. You can see that the angle of each reflection equals the angle at which

Fig. 21. The angle at which a ray of light reflects from a surface equals the angle at which it strikes.

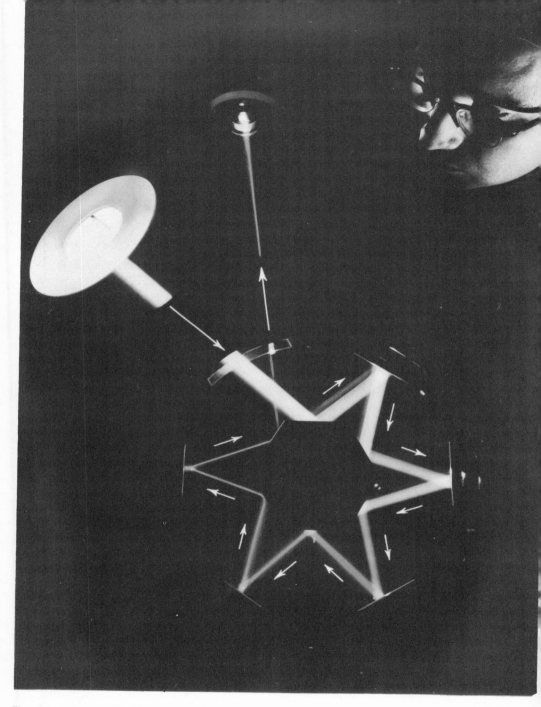

Fig. 22. Eleven reflections occur here, all at the same angle. (Westing-house Photo)

the beam strikes the mirror. It is also interesting to observe the way in which the beam becomes weaker as it bounces around the mirrors. This occurs because some light is lost at each reflection and also because cigarette smoke was blown into the path of the beam to make it visible. Reflection of light from the smoke reduced the brightness of the beam.

The process of reflection resembles the way in which a ball bounces off a wall. Try rolling a ball toward a wall along smooth, level ground. You will find that the ball bounces off the wall at the same angle at which it strikes. A good billiards player can figure out where to aim a ball that is to hit the side of the table by making use of the law of reflection.

Now let us see what causes a mirror image. In Fig. 23, MM represents a mirror. L represents a tiny lamp that produces a small spot of light and gives

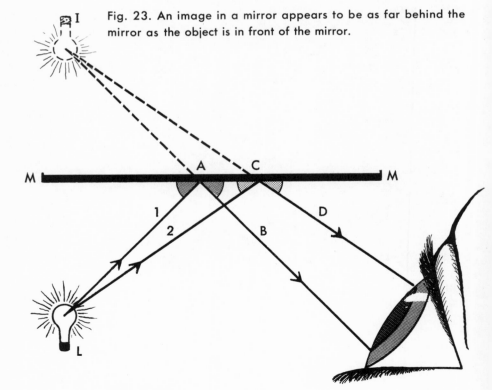

Fig. 23. An image in a mirror appears to be as far behind the mirror as the object is in front of the mirror.

out rays in all directions. Let us select two of these rays and study them carefully. One ray strikes the mirror at A. It bounces off at an equal angle to B and continues to the eye. The second ray strikes the mirror at C, bounces off at an equal angle to D, and enters the eye.

Where do these rays seem to come from? Extend the lines AB and CD back behind the mirror. If your drawing is accurate, you will find that the rays seem to meet at I, exactly as far behind the mirror as the light L is in front of it. I is an image of L.

Why is a mirror image reversed? In Fig. 24, three rays of light (1, 2, and 3) are bouncing off a mirror. After the first reflection, the order of the rays is 3, 2, 1. Thus the rays are reversed. The second reflection restores the beam to its original 1, 2, 3 order by means of a second reversal.

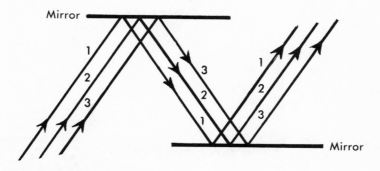

Fig. 24. The order of light rays is reversed at each reflection.

A mirror image is really an *optical illusion* by which you see something that is not really there. When you stand in front of a mirror, your reversed image is really not *you*. When you were a small

43

child, you were probably fooled by the first mirror images you saw, but now that you are familiar with them you know that they are just images.

Fig. 25 shows how we can still be fooled. When we look at the photograph we seem to see three panes of glass on a wall; through them we can see a door and two windows. But are they really glass? Perhaps they are mirrors reflecting an image of a door and windows? It is impossible to tell from this photograph. We may be looking at a reflection in a mirror or gazing through transparent glass. It is a perfect optical illusion.

Another optical illusion is shown in Fig. 26. Do you recognize it? Is it a totem pole? An ancient statue? Or is it a modern painting?

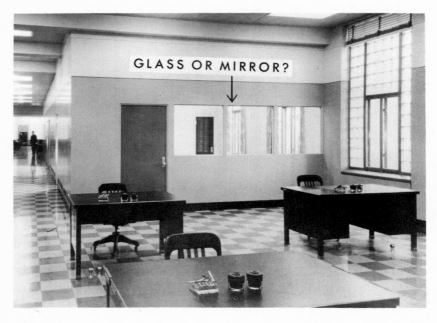

Fig. 25. An optical illusion. Are these mirrors or glass panels on the walls? (Johns-Manville Photo)

44

Fig. 26. What is it? A totem pole? (Wide World)

Turn the book around so that the small black circle is at the lower left-hand corner of the picture. Now look closely near the tip of the upper arrow. You see a tree. Look at the lower arrow. You see a reflected image of that tree. The "totem pole" is really a picture of the cliff wall at Grand Coulee Dam reflected in the quiet water of the lake. Notice that the reflection is almost identical with the cliff wall but is reversed. However, a disturbance in the water at the lower right-hand corner has produced a distortion and double image of the cliff.

CURVED MIRRORS

Fig. 27 is a mirror image of a photographer, a group of cadets, and several buildings as seen in the smooth, shiny helmet of one cadet. A surprising thing about this reflection is that it shows so many large objects in such a small mirror. Notice that everything seems smaller than normal and rather squeezed, and that the shapes of the objects are distorted.

Why does the mirror reflect such a large part of the surroundings? The shiny helmet is an example of a *convex* (outward-bulging) shape. A convex mirror always produces a small, crowded image that shows a large part of the surroundings. Fig. 28 explains why. Ray 1 comes from a building far to the left. It strikes the curved surface of the mirror, bounces off at an equal angle, and reaches the eye. To the eye the building appears to be at A, behind

Fig. 27. A convex mirror produces a small image of a large area. (Associated Press Photo)

the mirror. Ray 2, from another building far to the right, also enters the eye by bouncing off the right side of the mirror. This building appears to be at B

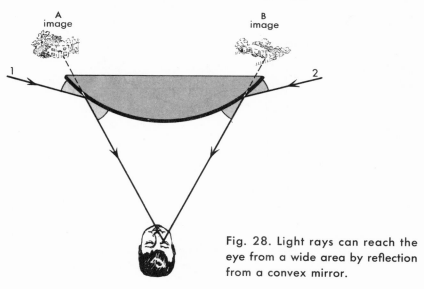

Fig. 28. Light rays can reach the eye from a wide area by reflection from a convex mirror.

47

Fig. 29. A concave mirror produces a large distorted image of a person near the mirror. (Wide World)

in the mirror. Thus we can see objects far to the left and the right in a convex mirror.

The ability of convex mirrors to reproduce small images of a large area makes them useful in certain types of rear-view mirrors for automobiles. They are often used in buses to enable the driver to see people getting off at the rear door.

The opposite effect occurs in the *concave* (inward-curving) mirror in Fig. 29. The girl in the picture is standing close to a large concave searchlight mirror, and we see a distorted enlargement of her face.

Fig. 30 shows how rays of light bounce off a concave mirror to reach the eye (or lens of a camera). Many rays of light are reflected from the top of the girl's head. But only ray 1 is in a position to re-

48

flect to the eye by bouncing off at an equal angle from the mirror. The eye then judges the top of the head to be somewhat near A.

In the same way, the ray that reaches the eye from the girl's chin reflects from the bottom of the mirror. The eye judges the image of her chin to be somewhere near B. You can see from Fig. 30 that the size of the image of the girl's head (AB) is much larger than its actual size. If the girl moves away from the mirror, the image enlarges, then seems to disappear, and finally becomes small and upside down. These interesting optical effects are put to use in reflecting telescopes.

Fig. 30. The reason for the enlarged image in a concave mirror may be found by tracing the light rays as they reflect at equal angles.

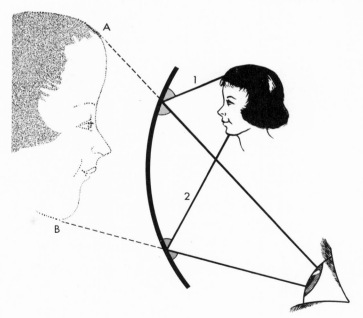

MIRROR PROBLEMS

1. How observant are you? Study the picture of painters on the scaffold in Fig. 17. Then try to answer these questions.

   a. How high is the scaffold?
   b. Are the painters working in the street or in a courtyard?
   c. Was the picture snapped early in the morning, at midday, or late in the afternoon?
   d. Are the painters working on a new building or an old one?
   e. Are they moving the scaffold or just holding the ropes still?
   f. Where was the photographer when the picture was snapped?

   Now compare your answers with those on pages 149 and 150.

2. Fig. 31 shows an interesting formation of images caused by placing two mirrors together at a 45° angle. Can you explain these images? Turn to page 150 for the answer.

Fig. 31. Two mirrors at a 45° angle produce seven images of an object.

5
Bending Light

IN Fig. 32 one pencil is made to look like many. Notice how the straight pencil appears to bend as it enters the water (A). There are additional images at B, C, D, E, F, G, and H. How do we explain this strange optical illusion?

Fig. 33 shows a beam of light passing through a triangular piece of glass. A glass this shape is called a *triangular prism.* We shall refer to the wide part of the prism near the bottom of the picture as the *base.* Notice that the beam of light is bent toward the base of the prism.

In Fig. 34 we see how rays of light bend as they pass through a solid rectangular block of glass. The rays bend in one direction as they enter the glass, and then bend by exactly the same amount, but in the opposite direction, as they leave the glass block. As a result the rays keep moving in the same direction. However, the paths of the rays are shifted to new positions. Thus when light passes through a piece of glass whose sides are parallel, there is a slight displacement but no change in direction.

Notice that there are slight reflections at each

Fig. 32. Why do you see so many pencils?

surface of the glass but that most of the light passes through.

Water, glass, and all other transparent materials act in the same way. Whenever light passes from one transparent material to another (at an angle), the rays always bend at the boundary. This type of bending of light rays is called *refraction*.

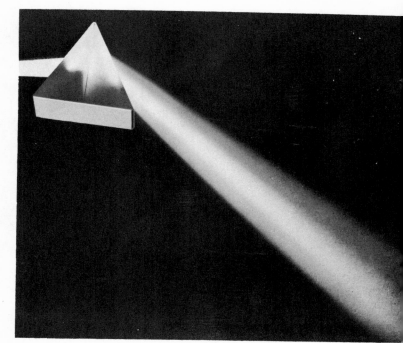

Fig. 33. A glass prism bends a beam of light. (Bausch and Lomb Optical Co.)

REFRACTION

Why do the legs of the man in Fig. 35 appear so short?

Look at Fig. 36. A ray of light from the man's feet at A travels upward at a glancing angle toward

Fig. 35. What causes the shortened appearance of legs in water?

54

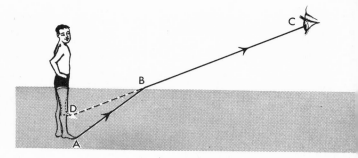

Fig. 36. Bending of light rays at the water surface causes the appearance of shortened legs.

the water's surface at B. It then bends toward the eye at C. The eye judges the ray to have traveled in a straight line and therefore sees the feet at D, higher than they really are.

Now let us return to the pencil in water (Fig. 32). As you look at the top of the water the pencil point appears higher than it actually is, for the same reason that the feet of the man in the water appear higher than they are. That is why the pencil looks bent when viewed through the upper surface of the water.

Fig. 37 is a view of the top of the same rectangular tank of water seen in Fig. 32. One ray of light from the pencil (A) reaches the eye (E) by traveling through the water to the side of the tank at B. It then bends toward E. The eye judges the ray to have come from straight back of B, at C. Similarly a ray from A, striking the other side of the tank at D, will bend toward the eye (E) and seem to come from F. Thus an image of the pencil appears in each side of the rectangular tank.

Light is also reflected from the four sides and the

Fig. 37. Refraction at each side of the tank causes extra images.

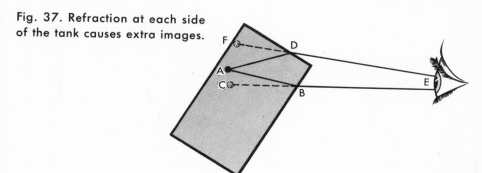

bottom of the tank and even from the underside of the water. In fact, there is always some reflection whenever light strikes the boundary between different materials. Five such reflections are seen in Fig. 32 (D, E, F, G, and H).

Try the experiment of putting a pencil into a transparent rectangular tank, as shown in Fig. 32. By looking at the tank from different positions, it is possible to see more than a dozen separate images.

REFRACTION IN EVERYDAY LIFE

The effects of refraction of light can be observed every day. For example, if you look carefully through an ordinary window the straight lines of distant buildings often appear bent and distorted. These distortions are due to imperfections in the glass. If the glass was perfectly flat and parallel on both sides, everything would appear straight. Light would then pass through without any change in direction, as it does in Fig. 34. Waviness in the glass makes it refract light so that the rays passing through change their direction slightly. As a result objects seen through the glass appear to be in somewhat different positions than they really are.

Refraction occurs in air as well as in water. Fig. 38 is a photograph of the sun taken from a mountaintop just before sunset. Notice that the sun looks somewhat flat. Light rays enter the earth's atmosphere from outer space. Just as the pencil seemed to bend when it was put into water, so the rays of the

Fig. 38. Refraction of light by the atmosphere causes the sun to appear flattened at sunset.

sun bend slightly as they go from one layer of the atmosphere to the next. This bending causes the sun to seem higher in the sky than it really is, just as the feet of the man standing in water (Fig. 35) seem to be higher than they actually are. The lower the sun is in the sky, the more its rays bend. Therefore, the bottom of the sun in Fig. 38 seems closer to the top, thus causing the sun to appear flattened.

Do the sun's rays ever strike the earth without bending? Notice that the light rays are not bent as they strike the prism at A in Fig. 39. The rays enter the glass at right angles to the surface. Only at a right angle can a light ray pass into a new material without bending. When the sun is directly overhead, its

Fig. 39. No bending occurs when light rays strike a surface at right angles. Notice how the beam is reflected from the inside surface. (Bausch and Lomb Optical Co.)

rays strike the earth's atmosphere at right angles, and light rays then enter the air without bending. At all other positions some bending of light occurs. Since the sun is directly overhead only in the tropics, nobody in the United States ever sees it exactly where it is in space.

The same thing holds true for the moon and the stars. When astronomers observe the stars and planets through large telescopes, they must take into account changes due to refraction. Such changes must be considered when rockets are aimed at the moon.

Fig. 39 tells us more about refraction. The three rays that strike surface A at right angles are completely reflected at surface B. They then strike C at right angles and get out of the prism without bending.

Why does this happen? In Fig. 40 a series of rays are coming from a source of light (A) inside a tank of water. Ray B strikes the water surface at a right angle and passes into the air without bending. Rays C, D, E, and F bend as they go into the air. Notice that ray F comes out almost parallel to the surface of the water. But ray G strikes the inside surface of the water at such an angle that it cannot be refracted into the air, and is reflected back into

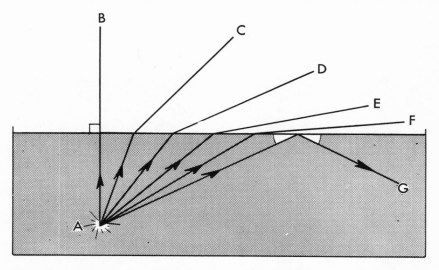

Fig. 40. A light ray is reflected as it strikes the inner surface of a transparent material at a glancing angle.

the water. Rays such as G, which strike the air-water surface from inside the water, are said to be beyond the *critical angle,* and are reflected rather than refracted.

Similar reflections, from the inside surface of glass, are shown in Fig. 41. Mirror reflections can be seen from the inside surfaces of the glass at A and at B. You can observe such reflections inside a glass of water or in a fish tank. Look upward at the under-surface of water in a glass. Then put your finger into the water and you will see its mirror reflection.

Prisms similar to the one in Fig. 39 are used as reflectors in binoculars and some telescopes. The metallic coatings of ordinary mirrors tend to corrode after a few years because of the chemical action of air, but a glass prism will last almost indefinitely. Therefore, the better optical instruments have prisms as reflectors rather than mirrors.

Fig. 41. Notice the mirror images caused by reflection of light from inside the glass at the bottom and left surface. (Corning Glass Works)

Fig. 42. The "pool of water" mirage is caused by refraction of light.

MIRAGES

While riding in a car on a sunny day you may have noticed a "pool of water" on the road ahead. But as your car approaches the puddle, the water disappears. The "water" is an optical illusion—a *mirage*. Fig. 42 is a photograph of such a mirage. The water that you seem to see under the distant car was not present at all at the time the photograph was taken. It was not even necessary to approach the "water" to make it disappear. Fig. 43 shows the same scene photographed a moment later with the camera raised a few feet. The "water" has practically disappeared.

Fig. 43. When the camera was raised a few feet, the mirage in Fig. 42 disappeared.

Why does this happen? On a sunny day the road heats up and the layer of air just above it becomes very warm. The air a bit higher remains cool. The different kinds of air (cool air and warm air) cause light to bend, just as it bends when passing from air into water.

Fig. 44 shows the way in which the light bends. Rays moving almost parallel to the ground and

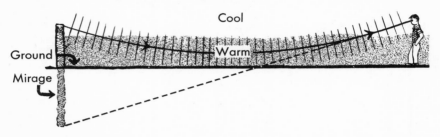

Fig. 44. Light rays cause the mirage in Fig. 42 by bending upward as they pass from warm to cool air.

slightly downward are bent so that they travel up toward your eye. You then think that the rays of light come from the ground.

Why do you get the illusion of water? A distant pool of water will reflect rays of light from the sky and make them bounce up toward your eye. You then see a bright area of light that appears to come from the ground. You learn by experience that such bright areas are simply reflections of light from water. Therefore, when you see a similar bright area in the road caused by refraction, it looks so much like a reflection from water that you think it is caused by water.

You may have read how travelers lost in the desert sometimes see water ahead and run toward it,

Fig. 45. This "castles-in-the-air" mirage occurred over a cool, flat, swampy area. (Wide World)

only to have it disappear. They are attracted by a mirage similar to the kind you see in a road. The long, flat, hot stretches of desert increase the effect, and a mirage of an entire lake may appear in the sands.

A different kind of mirage is seen in Fig. 45. Trees and houses appear in the sky high above the horizon. The sky mirage is the opposite of the pool-of-

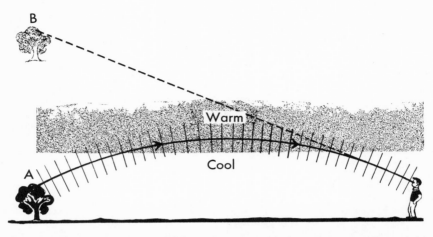

Fig. 46. The mirage is caused by refraction of light as it passes from cold air near the ground to warm air above.

water mirage. It appears above the horizon rather than below it, and is caused by cold air near the ground rather than by warm air. It sometimes appears over a flat, swampy area, where water in the swamp cools the warm air just above the ground. Fig. 46 shows how the light coming from a distant tree (A) bends as it passes from cool air to warm air. The eye sees the light coming from above the horizon at B. An enlarging effect may also occur similar to that produced by a magnifying glass. The result is the enlarged, ghostly image of trees and houses in mid-air.

A similar effect causes the twinkling of stars. As light from a star passes through the atmosphere, it encounters moving currents of warm and cold air. The light wave is refracted and its direction changed slightly as it passes from one kind of air to the other. And, since the layers of warm and cool air move around, the star seems to shift its position rapidly. In other words, it twinkles.

The same effect may be observed by looking over the top of a hot radiator, or the top of a dark-colored car standing out in the sun. Objects seen across the top of the hot radiator or car seem to shimmer and wiggle because of the changing refraction of light as it passes from moving cold air to warm air.

Notice the shadow cast by a hot radiator, stove, or flame when it is in sunlight. Look at the wall or floor just above the hot part. You see a moving, wavy pattern of dark lines. These lines are caused by the refraction of the sun's light as it passes from cold to warm air and back to cold air.

REFRACTION PROBLEMS

1. The metal ball in Fig. 47 is traveling at a speed of 10,000 miles per hour. What causes the curved lines that are seen in the air around the ball? How can we photograph anything going so fast?

Fig. 47. The waves caused by this bullet, traveling 10,000 miles per hour, are made visible by refraction of light passing through its shock wave. (National Advisory Committee for Aeronautics)

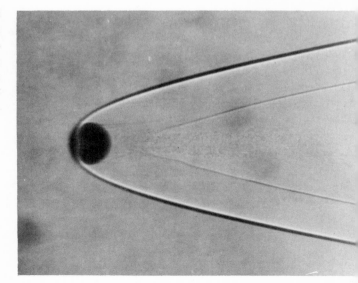

2. The girl in Fig. 48 is breathing out air under water. Since we live in an ocean of air, it is usually invisible, while water is visible. But in Fig. 48 the situation is reversed. The air is visible, while the water is invisible. Why?

Now compare your answers with those on pages 150 and 151.

Fig. 48. Why is the air visible and the water almost invisible? (United States Rubber Co.)

PART II

Different Kinds of Light

What is light?

You may think that this is not a practical question. But, in fact, the study of the nature of light has led to our giant radio, TV, X-ray, radar, and other electronics industries. Atomic energy could not have been developed without a knowledge of the nature of light.

Scientists classify visible light as just one of many different kinds of "electromagnetic waves." Fig. 49 is a chart of these waves. The small, dark section just below the middle of the chart represents the region of visible light. Above and below it are other electromagnetic waves, very similar to light. You might call them "invisible light."

None of these types of light were known before the year 1800. Since that time scientists in many lands have pushed the boundaries of our knowledge outward. As a result there are today thousands upon thousands of practical uses for the new kinds of invisible light that have been discovered. Some of these uses are indicated in Fig. 49.

How were these forms of invisible light discovered? You will find out in the chapters that follow.

THE SPECTRUM OF ELECTROMAGNETIC WAVES

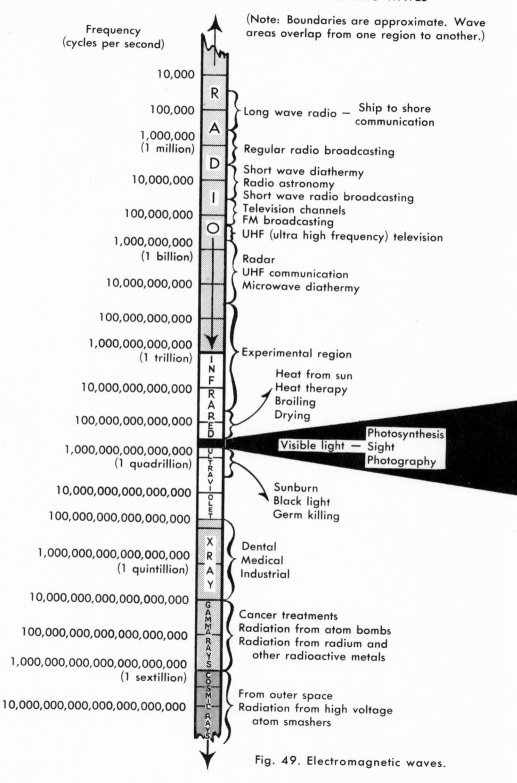

Fig. 49. Electromagnetic waves.

6 Light Waves

WHY does light bend as it passes from air into transparent materials such as water or glass? Why is light reflected when it strikes objects?

In the seventeenth century two different explanations of the behavior of light were debated by scientists. Christian Huygens thought that light was some kind of wave. On the other hand, Isaac Newton believed that light consisted of a stream of bulletlike particles.

Huygens got his idea for light waves by observing the way in which water waves behave. Fig. 50 is a photograph of a water wave made in a shallow glass tank. The camera was placed above the tank

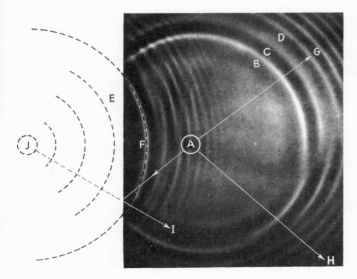

Fig. 50. The motions of light waves greatly resemble those of water waves. (Physical Science Study Committee)

and a light below it. The circular area (A) is the place from which the waves start.

Notice how waves B, C, and D spread outward in the form of a series of circles with their centers at the starting point A. Observe how the wave is reflected from wall E at the left side of the tank in such a way that it reverses direction but still keeps its circular shape (F).

According to Huygens, a light *ray* is simply *the direction in which the wave travels,* as shown by the straight lines G and H in Fig. 50. The direction of the reflected wave at I follows the rule that a reflected ray bounces off a surface at the same angle it strikes the surface. And notice that J, the point from which the new wave seems to come, is as far behind the reflecting surface as A, the starting point of the original wave, was in front of it. These properties of reflected water waves seem to match those of reflected light.

According to the wave theory of light, a luminous object like a lamp or the sun is one that gives off continuous series of waves, one after the other, very much like those in Fig. 50. However, such waves would be pictured as traveling outward in a spherical (ball-shaped) form, rather than in flat circles like the water waves in Fig. 50.

How is refraction explained by the wave theory?

Fig. 51 is a photograph of straight water waves traveling from left to right in a flat tank. The section of the tank to the right of the line AB is built so that it is shallower than the section on the left. As a result the waves slow down when they reach

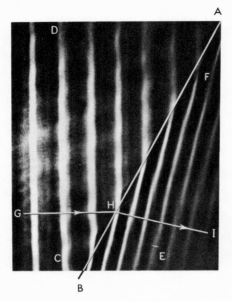

Fig. 51. Refraction is caused by reduced speed as a wave reaches an obstacle. (Physical Science Study Committee)

AB. The lower part of a wave (C) arrives at the shallow section sooner than the upper part (D). As a result part C is slowed down, while the upper part (D) continues at the same speed. Thus the upper part of the wave advances farther than the lower part. The wave then swings around, changes its direction, and is refracted. The original direction of motion (GH) changes after the wave (EF) enters the shallow, slow part of the tank. The new direction of the wave is HI.

Huygens said that light is refracted when it passes from air into water or glass because the part of the wave in the new transparent material slows down, swerves, and changes direction, just like the water wave in Fig. 51. On the way out the bending occurs in the opposite direction because the wave speeds up as it goes from water or glass into air.

It is easy to explain the refraction that occurs in mirages by using Huygens' wave theory. Fig. 44 shows the waves as almost vertical lines. The tops of the waves, in cool, heavier air, move a bit more slowly than the bottoms, traveling in light, warm air. Thus the wave swerves and bends upward.

This process resembles the way in which a line of marchers in a parade goes around a corner. The man on the inside slows down, while the man on the outside maintains his pace. As a result the entire line swings around and changes direction.

Study Fig. 46, which shows a mirage in which light bends downward. In this case the cool, heavier air is below the warm, light air. The bottoms of the waves therefore slow down and they bend toward the ground.

WAVES OR PARTICLES?

Huygens' theory that light is a wave motion seems to explain reflection and refraction. But it does not *prove* that the theory is right. Isaac Newton believed that light was made up of bulletlike particles that bounced off objects to cause reflection of light. He explained refraction by imagining that there is a force of attraction that pulls a light particle as it approaches a material. The material will then pull a particle away from a straight path closer to itself, thereby causing refraction.

According to Newton, the particle of light, which he called a "corpuscle," would be speeded up by the attraction of a transparent material as it passed into it from air. But according to Huygens, a light wave had to slow up when passing from air into a transparent material. One way to find out who was right was to measure the speed of light in a material. But scientists did not have the equipment to do this in Newton's time.

Mainly because of the great respect scientists had for Newton, they accepted his theory rather than that of Huygens. However, in the early part of the nineteenth century, experiments were performed that seemed to favor the wave theory. Scientific opinion began to shift. Then around 1850, the speed of light was measured in water. It was shown to be less than in air. This seemed to prove that the wave theory was correct beyond any doubt.

INTERFERENCE OF LIGHT

One of the strongest arguments for the wave theory is an optical effect known as *interference*. Look at the pattern of the two sets of water waves in Fig. 52. The waves radiate outward from the points A and B, and then pass through each other. You will notice that at some places the wave from A seems to join with the wave from B to make a strong wave (C, D, E). But at other places (F, G, H) the waves join in such a way that they seem to cancel each other out and cause a quiet area. Why does this happen?

Fig. 53 shows a typical wave. It consists of

74

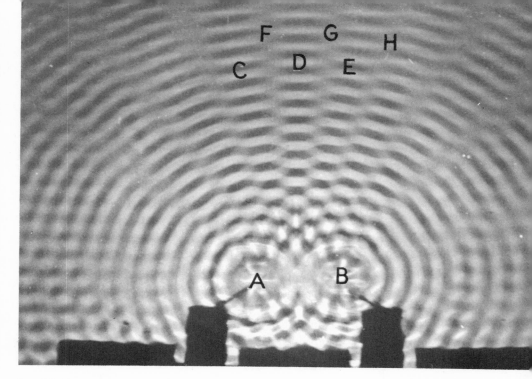

Fig. 52. Waves from two different sources can "interfere" and cancel each other where the crest of one wave meets the trough of another. (Physical Science Study Committee)

a series of high parts or *crests,* followed by low parts, or *troughs.* An object floating on the water will move up with the crest of one wave and down with the trough. But suppose that the crest of one wave and the trough of an equally strong wave arrive at the same place at the same time. The waves will

Fig. 53. A wave consists of a succession of crests and troughs.

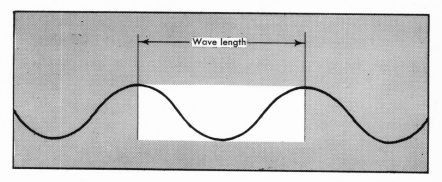

then *interfere*. The upward motion of the crest from one wave will be canceled out by downward motion of the trough from the other. If the two sets of waves have the same wave length (distance between crests), the region where crests meet troughs will be still, even though waves are passing through all the time! F, G, and H are the regions of still water in Fig. 52. The regions of wavy water (C, D, E) are those where crests meet crests and troughs meet troughs.

The wave theory of light proves quite useful in such a practical matter as the manufacture of precision machinery and optical intruments of high quality, where it is necessary to measure lengths with great accuracy. Fig. 54 shows how interference of light is used in making an "optical flat" that is accurate to within a millionth of an inch. An instrument known as an *interferometer* compares the light patterns formed by reflection from a standard optical flat with the one being manufactured. In some areas the crests of light waves from one flat meet the crests from the other to form bright bands. In other areas the crests meet troughs and interfere to form dark bands. Slight imperfections in the surface cause a wavy pattern (Fig. 54A). The nature of the wavy pattern gives a clue about how the flat surface should be polished. Finally, after proper polishing, the pattern appears as in Fig. 54B. The glass disc is now accurately flat to within a millionth of an inch.

The way in which the wave theory of light explains interference is very strong evidence that the

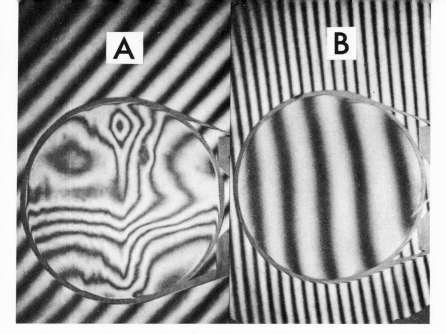

Fig. 54. Interference of light is put to practical use in making "optical flats." The straight lines in B show that the surface is accurately flat to one millionth of an inch. (Northrop Aircraft)

theory is correct. Nobody has been able to explain interference in a satisfactory way by the particle theory of light.

POLARIZATION

Additional evidence for the wave theory is provided by *polarization* of light.

In Fig. 55, light is reflected from a surface behind two polarizing disks. Notice that you can see the striped background through the disks, where they do not overlap. But where they overlap there is a dense black area, and no light comes through.

We would expect the overlapping area to appear darker, but why is the light blocked completely? If each disk lets through a portion of the light reach-

77

ing it, why shouldn't at least some light come through the overlapped disks? But it doesn't. Moreover, when one disk is given a quarter turn (90°), the light comes through both and the black area disappears.

It is difficult to see how it would make any difference to a bulletlike particle whether a sheet of material through which it was passing was turned or not. But it does make a difference to a wave.

Let us picture the situation in terms of a wave in a rope. Fig. 56 shows a wave produced in a rope, passing through two slotted boards A and B. The up-and-down rope waves easily go through the vertical slot of board A. But the slot in board B is horizontal, across the up-and-down motion of the rope, and the wave cannot get through. Thus the section of the rope between board B and the hook always remains straight.

Suppose that the board B is given a quarter turn

78

and made vertical. It would then let the wave come through.

A wave is said to be "polarized" when it vibrates in one direction. Normally, light waves are unpolarized. Some are like water waves and vibrate up and down as they move forward; others vibrate from side to side. When light waves pass through a piece of polarizing material, they come through vibrating in only one direction. They are polarized. If polarized waves reach another piece of polarized material, they will be stopped completely if the second piece is placed with its "slots" at right angles to the first one. But if the polarizing pieces are parallel to each other, the waves will get through.

A DOUBLE STANDARD

It might appear that the case for the wave theory of light has been proved. And so it seemed before

Fig. 56. A wave in a rope will pass through a slot in a board only if the slot is parallel to the vibration of the wave.

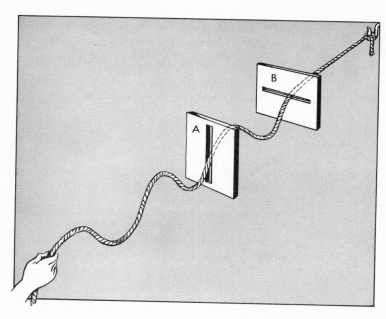

1900. But later in the book we shall give some of the evidence that points to the existence of packages or bundles of light energy. Scientists are now in the peculiar position of sometimes using the wave theory and at other times a particle theory. They look forward to the time when some genius will work out a theory that will explain light more completely.

In our next chapter we shall see how the wave theory helps to explain color.

ILLUSION PROBLEM

Fig. 57 shows two glass tubes standing in a jar half full of liquid. A strange thing has happened to one of the tubes—it has disappeared in the liquid. Try to figure out why. Then turn to page 151 for the answer.

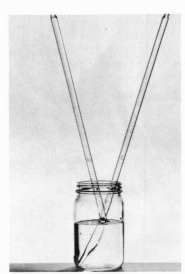

Fig. 57. Why does one glass rod disappear in the liquid? (Fisher Scientific Co.)

7

Color and the Spectrum

COLOR plays an important part in our lives. We spend billions of dollars each year to make our homes, clothes, furniture, magazines, and posters more colorful, and therefore more pleasing. Yet few of us stop to ask the question, "What is color?"

Chemists can analyze the chemical contents of a complicated material by studying colors it produces in a flame. A detective can use this process to tell whether a particular bit of dirt on a suspect's shoe came from the scene of a crime. The nature and structure of atoms can be figured out by analyzing color, and this information has helped to develop theories about atomic energy.

WHAT IS COLOR?

Isaac Newton performed experiments in 1669 that became the basis for much of our knowledge about color. He observed a narrow beam of light passing through a triangular glass prism (Fig. 58). The white light split into a colored beam, a *spectrum,*

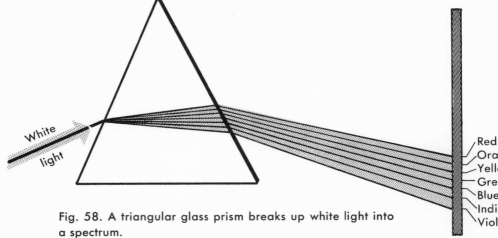

Fig. 58. A triangular glass prism breaks up white light into a spectrum.

made up of the following colors: red, orange, yellow, green, blue, indigo, and violet. Newton then put the colors together again to form the original white light. But when he tried to break up each of the colors in the spectrum still further, he did not succeed. The colors in the spectrum seemed to be basic. He concluded that white light is composed of all the colors in the spectrum.

What causes differences in color? Newton thought that there were different kinds of light "bullets." One kind produced the effect of red, another blue, and so forth. According to Huygens' wave theory, which we accept today, the different colors could be explained by assuming that each kind of wave had its own *frequency* (Fig. 59). Frequency is the number of vibrations per second in the wave. For example, if you stand in water and count the waves that go by, you will find that different waves have different frequencies. In one minute you might count 100 ripples reaching your leg. The frequency would be 100 waves per minute. But if a boat should go by,

82

it would cause waves of a lower frequency. Then perhaps only ten waves would reach you in a minute.

Closely connected with the idea of frequency is that of *wave length.* We have seen that one wave length is the distance between the crest of one wave and the crest of the next one. Fig. 59 shows two waves. A has more ups and downs (more waves) than B. Wave A therefore has a higher frequency. Now notice their wave length. The crests of wave A are closer together than those of wave B; therefore the wave length of A is less than that of B. A *higher frequency* (more waves) means a *lower wave length* (waves closer together).

Scientists are able to measure the wave length and frequency of the different colors in the spectrum. Red light waves have a frequency of 375 trillion waves per second, and violet waves 750 trillion! The wave length of red light is about 1/30,000 inch, and that of violet about 1/65,000 inch.

Why does a spectrum form when white light passes through a triangular glass prism? Fig. 33

Fig. 59. High-frequency waves have short wave lengths. Low-frequency waves have long wave lengths.

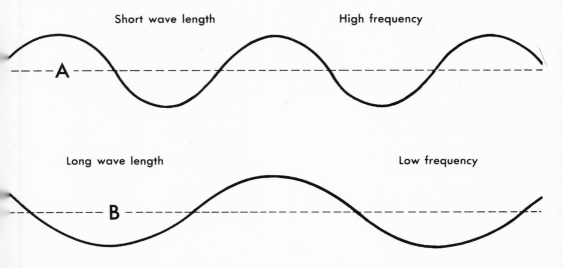

Short wave length   High frequency

A

Long wave length   Low frequency

B

shows a beam of light bending as it passes through a triangular glass prism. And in Chapter 6 we learned that a beam of light bends (is refracted) when it enters glass because it slows down. Violet light waves slow down more than red; therefore they bend more. The red and violet waves in a beam of white light therefore reach different places on a screen after they pass through the prism. This separation of the colors of white light into a spectrum is called *dispersion*.

EXPLAINING COLORS

Why do some objects appear red, others green, and still others blue? A red object reflects red light, and little green or blue light. When you look at a red object you see the red light but not the other colors. In the same way a green object reflects mainly green light, a blue object mainly blue light. A white object reflects all colors. A black object reflects no light. A gray object reflects about half of the white light that reaches it.

What happens to the colors that are not reflected? They are *absorbed* by the object. The energy of such absorbed waves is turned into heat. Thus the darker the color, the more it will heat up in sunlight.

Many different combinations of colors may be reflected. For example, an object that reflects red and blue but not green appears purple. An object that reflects blue and green but not red appears bluish-green. An object that reflects red and green appears yellow.

A color is dark or light according to the percentage of light it reflects. For example, an object that reflects 90 per cent of the red light striking it and 70 per cent of all other colors looks reddish-tinted white, or pink. On the other hand, an object that reflects about 50 per cent of the red and green and only 20 per cent of the blue looks dark yellow, or tan. The enormous varieties of colors that we observe—brown, mauve, cerise, aquamarine, dark red, light blue, lemon yellow, and so on—are due to the different percentages of reflection of the different colors in the spectrum.

The color we see also depends upon the way in which the brain interprets the signals it receives from the eye. Recent experiments indicate that the psychology of color vision plays a very important part in determining the particular colors we see when different patterns of colored light enter the eye.

COLOR IN NATURE

Have you ever made a rainbow? It's quite easy! Just stand with your back to the late-afternoon sun and spray water in front of you with a garden hose. Or if you are standing in water turn your back to the sun and splash water in front of you. A circular rainbow will appear in the spray. It is the same kind

Fig. 60. Rainbows are caused by reflections and refractions from billions of droplets in a rain cloud. (U.S. Weather Bureau)

of rainbow as that formed by a rain cloud in the late-afternoon sun (Fig. 60).

A rainbow appears when white light from the sun is separated into its spectrum colors as it passes through water droplets in the air. You can see a rainbow only when the sun is shining behind you. Rays of sunlight striking the billions of water droplets in a rain cloud are refracted as they enter each droplet. The different-colored waves in the sunlight bend a certain amount, and are *dispersed* or spread apart. These rays then reflect from the back surfaces of the raindrops toward your eye. The various-colored waves arrive at your eye from different directions because of dispersion. But they can reach your eye only if there is a certain angle between you and the droplet and the sun. Therefore you see a ring of red color in the sky wherever droplets are in just the right position to send red waves to your eye. Violet waves arrive from another position, and you see a separate ring of violet light. The same thing is true of the other colors. Therefore a circular spectrum—or rainbow—appears in the sky.

In Fig. 60 there is a second rainbow (A) around the main one (B). A double rainbow is formed by double reflections inside the droplets. On rare occasions more than two rainbow rings are seen when the light rays take different paths inside the droplets. The additional rainbow rings at C in Fig. 60 were formed in this way.

Why is the sky blue? Why does the sun appear red when it rises or sets? These questions are closely connected. As rays of light pass through the air, they meet dust particles and tiny drops of water. Some of the light is absorbed and turned into heat, some is scattered, and the rest passes straight through. Now the blue light in sunlight is scattered much more than the red and more of the red light goes straight through.

When the sun is low in the sky, the light must pass through a greater thickness of air than when the sun is overhead. In the long journey through the air a great deal of light is scattered sideward. For that reason you can look directly at the sun at sunset, but not when it is overhead. And since more blue light is scattered than red, a higher percentage of red light goes straight through and the sun appears red at sunset.

What happens to the blue light that does not get through? Most of it is scattered in all directions by the dust particles. As a result we see blue light coming from all parts of the sky, and the sky appears blue.

What does the sky look like out in space? Since there is no dust in the air to scatter the blue rays, the sky is not blue at all; it is jet black. Space travelers will see the stars in a jet-black sky, even with the sun shining brightly.

THE SPECTRUM

How many colors are there? There are so many different colors that they can't be counted. In the first place one light wave is a different color if it has a slightly different frequency than another wave. We can also combine the various frequencies in many different ways. Thus we can say that the number of colors is practically *infinite* (so great that it cannot be counted).

This does not mean that we can *see* how all the colors differ. Our eyes can distinguish differences only between broad ranges of color and not between frequencies close together. But with the aid of an instrument called a *spectroscope* we can analyze the colors in any kind of light. The spectroscope is one of the most useful instruments known to science.

One type of spectroscope makes use of a triangular glass prism. The prism breaks up a beam of light into the different colors (frequencies) and spreads them out in the form of a spectrum, as we have seen in Fig. 58. Lenses are used to form clear and sharp images of this spectrum, which may then be examined with the eye or photographed.

The spectrum of light of an incandescent lamp shows nothing unusual. The broad bands of color range from red to violet. Such a spectrum is called *continuous.* But if we take any substance and heat it sufficiently in a flame, or place it in the center of an electric spark, then the spectrum becomes *a bright-line spectrum,* composed of separate colored lines. Each substance has its own pattern of colored lines in the spectrum. We can study the spectrum-line pattern of a substance and use it as a "fingerprint" to detect the presence of that substance.

Fig. 61A is a very small portion of a spectrum formed by iron burned in a spark. The bright lines that you see are found in these positions only in the spectrum of iron. Directly below it (Fig. 61B) is a spectrum of the sun's light taken with the same instrument.

Notice that the sun's spectrum contains dark lines on a light background, while the iron spectrum contains bright lines on a dark background. For every bright line in the iron spectrum there is a dark line

Fig. 61. Iron spectrum lines (A) in the spectrum of the sun (B) reveal the presence of iron in the sun. (Mount Wilson and Palomar Observatories)

in the same place in the sun's spectrum. What does this mean?

A bright-line spectrum is formed whenever a substance is heated to a gaseous state at very high temperature. But what happens if white light is sent through a relatively cool gas of a substance? We then find that the cool gas absorbs the same frequencies of light that it would emit (send forth) if it were very hot. These absorbed frequencies (colors) are then subtracted from the white light passing through. Therefore, the resulting spectrum appears with dark lines. Such a spectrum is called an *absorption spectrum* or *dark-line spectrum.* The dark-line "fingerprints" in the spectrum of a substance occur in the same places as they would appear in a bright-line spectrum for that substance.

The sun consists of an enormous ball of hot gas. Its surface gives out a bright continuous spectrum of white light. But it is surrounded by relatively cooler layers of gas containing many different substances. Each substance then absorbs particular frequencies. Thus, as we view the spectrum of the sun, we see dark lines for each substance in the cool outer layers of the sun.

Does the sun contain iron? Dark lines for iron appear in the sun's spectrum (Fig. 61). Therefore we are quite sure that there is iron in the sun. In the same manner, more than sixty *elements* (basic substances) found on the earth have also been found in the sun.

One substance, *helium,* was found in the sun before it was found on earth! A pattern of lines appeared in the sun's spectrum which was produced by no substance known on earth. A hunt then started to find a material that formed the same spectrum. Finally, it was found in a gas given off at some oil wells. When the gas was analyzed, one part of it gave the same spectrum as that noted on the sun. The substance was named helium after the Greek sun god, Helios.

The spectra of most of the substances found on earth have been carefully catalogued and published in books. If a bit of a substance is burned in a spark or flame and the spectrum analyzed, it is possible to compare the spectrum lines with those of the substances listed in the catalogue. We can then tell what substances the material contains.

Suppose that a detective suspects someone of having committed a burglary. A window has been jimmied open with a tool. The detective finds a crowbar in the suspect's car and notices that a bit of paint on the crowbar is the same color as the window frame. This is a clue that the suspect used the crowbar on the window, but it isn't proof. The detective sends small samples of the paint on the crowbar and on the window frame to the laboratory. The samples are burned in a spark and the spectra are photographed. If both spectra show exactly the same lines, then we are practically certain that the paint on the crowbar and on the window frame is the same, and we have strong evidence that the suspect used the crowbar to open the window.

The spectroscope is amazingly accurate. For example, the spectrum in Fig. 61 is a small portion of a large one, thirteen feet long. When a photograph of such a large spectrum is examined with a microscope, tens of thousands of lines can be identified and measured accurately. In this way even a tiny trace of a substance can be detected and the amount estimated from the appearance of the lines.

COLOR IN ASTRONOMY

Some stars are red, others yellow, and still others white. Astronomers have learned to classify the stars according to color and spectrum. From this information about a star they can tell if it is a very hot star or a cool star, a giant or a dwarf.

The spectrum of a star enables us to tell whether it is approaching the earth or moving away, and how fast. How is this done?

Fig. 62A is a photograph of a portion of a spectrum of the bright star Arcturus. Directly below it (B) is a spectrum of iron. The vertical arrows show that dark lines for iron appear in the spectrum of Arcturus, but they are all shifted slightly toward the violet end of the spectrum. An astronomer would interpret this shift to the violet as meaning that Arcturus was moving toward us at the time the spectrum photograph was taken. When the amount of shift is measured, it is possible to tell how fast the star was approaching. In Fig. 62 the amount of shift indicated that Arcturus was moving toward us with a speed of about twenty miles a second at the time the picture was taken.

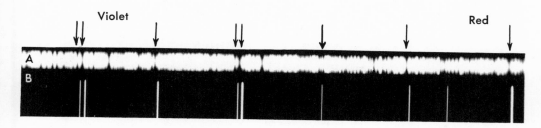

Fig. 62. A shift of the spectrum lines of a star toward the violet indicates that it is approaching us. (Mount Wilson and Palomar Observatories)

Why does this shift occur? Suppose that a star is moving toward us. Picture the "crest" of a light wave starting out from a particular spot on the star at a certain moment. This wave crest is followed by another a brief instant later. But by the time the second wave crest comes out, the star has moved slightly toward us. As a result, the distance between waves is a bit less than it would be if the star were still. This means that the wave length is less and that the color has shifted a bit to the violet (short wave length) end of the spectrum. The faster the star moves toward us, the greater the shift toward the violet.

On the other hand, if the star moves away from us, the distance between waves will be a bit greater than normal and the spectrum lines will shift toward the red. This is known as the *Doppler effect*.

The measurement of spectra has led to important theories about the beginnings of the universe. Fig. 63A shows a galaxy, a large group of about a billion very distant stars. Fig. 63B shows its spectrum. The white arrow points to a section of the spectrum with two dark lines. By measuring the amount of shift of these dark spectrum lines toward the red, astronomers know that the galaxy is traveling away from the earth at a speed of 750 miles a second.

Fig. 63C shows a much more distant galaxy. It is so far away that its light waves take 350 million years to reach us! It is said to be at a distance of 350 million *light-years*. The horizontal arrow pointing toward D shows the amount of shift of the spectrum lines in the direction of the red. The galaxy is moving away from us at the rate of 38,000 miles a second—about one-fifth the speed of light.

Similar measurements of other distant galaxies show that all of them are moving away from us. And the farther they are, the faster they seem to move away.

What does all this mean? Imagine that the entire universe once consisted of a small, very hot, very compact bundle of matter. Imagine, too, that it suddenly exploded in the most violent explosion of all time. Some parts moved out from the center of the

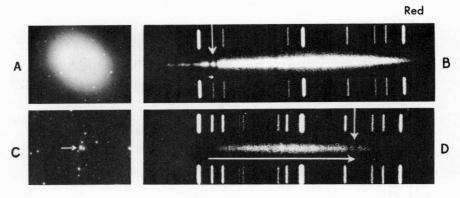

Fig. 63. The spectra (B and D) from distant galaxies (A and C) show large shifts of lines toward the red, thus indicating that they are speeding away from us at enormous velocities. (Mount Wilson and Palomar Observatories)

explosion faster than others. According to the principle of *inertia,* each bit of matter keeps going at the same speed in a straight line. There is no rubbing or friction out in space; and once started, the motion of an object continues *forever,* unless the object is pulled back in some manner.

Many astronomers think that an explosion in the remote past caused the enormous speeds at which these distant galaxies move. This would explain why the most distant galaxies have the highest speeds.

When did such an explosion occur? Did it really happen? From the distance and speed of the galaxies we can figure out how long they may have been moving away. It turns out to be more than 5 billion years!

Did our universe begin at that time?

The ages of rocks can be measured by radioactivity. The age of the ocean can be calculated from the amount of salt it contains. These estimates, plus other evidence, indicate that the earth is about 4 billion years old. If the universe is 5 billion years old, there would seem to be enough time for the sun and earth to have formed and for the earth to have cooled until it formed oceans and continents.

But perhaps the shift of the spectrum lines toward the red is because of something else. Might it not be caused by some unknown effect as the light travels for tens and hundreds of millions of years through space? Perhaps. Only time and more scientific research can answer this question.

ATOMS AND SPECTRA

You have probably seen the picture of an atom in which particles of matter called *electrons* whirl in orbits around a central *nucleus*. It has become a symbol for science and atomic energy.

This picture of the orbits of atoms was developed by the Danish scientist Niels Bohr in 1913. The clue to these orbits was provided by the lines in the spectrum of a star similar to the one shown in Fig. 64. Notice how the lines come closer and closer together toward the left end, up to a certain point. This is part of a regular group of spectrum lines called the *Balmer series.*

Bohr was able to explain these lines with great accuracy, using the theory that they are caused by electrons jumping from outer orbits to inner ones. With each jump from one orbit to another, an electron sends out light of a particular color (frequency).

Today, spectrum measurements are one of the main methods by which scientists obtain information about atoms. It is probable that we would not yet have achieved practical uses for atomic energy without the studies made with the spectroscope.

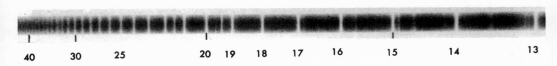

| 40 | 30 | 25 | 20 | 19 | 18 | 17 | 16 | 15 | 14 | 13 |

Fig. 64. Our picture of the atom was constructed with the aid of the spectrum lines in this "Balmer series." (Mount Wilson and Palomar Observatories)

COLOR PROBLEM

Expert photographers use different colored glass filters over the lenses of their cameras to produce different effects. Fig. 65B shows what happens when the camera lens is covered with a yellow filter. Compare the photograph with Fig. 65A, taken without a filter.

Why does the sky appear much darker in the photograph taken with a yellow filter?

Now test your powers of observation by answering these questions.

a. In which picture was the sun hidden by a cloud?
b. Is the wind speed steady or changing?
c. Did the wind shift direction?
d. What is the weather like? Is the air humid or dry?
e. What is the time of day (approximately)?

Fig. 65. The use of a yellow filter produced greater contrast in the clouds. (Eastman Kodak)

f. In what direction was the camera facing?
g. Which picture was taken first?
h. In what direction are the clouds moving?
i. Were the pictures taken at different times of the day?
j. Are all clouds moving in the same way?
k. Was the camera moved?

Compare your answers with those on page 152.

SPECTRUM PROBLEM

Fig. 66 shows the spectrum of one of the stars in the handle of the Big Dipper. Spectrum B was taken two days after spectrum A. The arrows show how single lines in spectrum A split into two lines in spectrum B. The spectrum lines will come together again at a later date. Still later they will separate. This process is repeated every 20.5 days.

How do you explain this spectrum mystery?

Turn to page 153 for the answer.

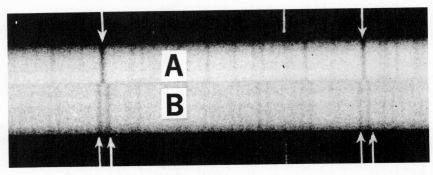

Fig. 66. Splitting of the spectrum lines from a star (B) reveals the fact that two stars are rotating around each other. (Mount Wilson and Palomar Observatories)

8

Invisible "Light"

Can you see in the dark? What a silly question!
But it really isn't so silly. The fact is, you *can* see
in the dark, if you have the proper equipment. You
will need a source of "invisible light" and some
means of detecting it.

Fig. 67 is a good example of what we mean. The
women are processing photographic film. Since ordinary light would ruin the film, they must work
in the dark. You will notice that they seem to be
looking straight ahead even though the work is below their eyes. They can't see in the dark anyway, so
there is no point in looking down.

How was the picture taken? A special lamp gave
off a powerful beam of invisible *infrared* waves and
the camera used a special film sensitive to these
waves. Thus the picture was taken in the dark.

If infrared waves are invisible, how were they
found? It all started in 1800 with William Herschel,
who discovered the planet Uranus. Herschel knew
that the sun's light caused heat when it struck an
object and he wondered whether the different colors
in white light had different heating effects. So he

placed a thermometer in the path of the spectrum produced by a prism. He found that red light heated the thermometer more than violet. But when he moved the thermometer into the invisible region past the red, he found the heat increased! These invisible heat rays are now called *infrared* rays or waves (Fig. 68). The prefix "infra" means below. The rays are really "below the red" rays in the spectrum; that is, they are waves of lower frequency than red.

Invisible rays were also found beyond the violet light at the opposite end of the spectrum (Fig. 68).

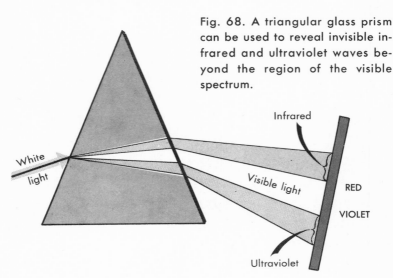

Fig. 68. A triangular glass prism can be used to reveal invisible infrared and ultraviolet waves beyond the region of the visible spectrum.

White light

Infrared

Visible light

RED

VIOLET

Ultraviolet

These rays are called *ultraviolet*. The prefix "ultra" means beyond. Therefore ultraviolet waves are really "beyond the violet" waves.

What would the world look like if we could see it with infrared waves? Fig. 69 shows two aerial photographs. The one on the left was taken with ordinary film. But the one on the right was taken with special "filters" that absorbed regular light and let only infrared waves into the camera.

Notice that the general outline of the roads, fields, and forests appears the same. But the blacks, whites, and grays are very different. For example, the letters A and B show a small pond. In the "regular light" photo on the left, the pond appears gray against a darker background. This happens because the water

Fig. 69. The world looks very different in infrared light as shown by the aerial picture on right. (Fairchild Camera and Instrument Corp.)

of the pond reflects slightly more light to the camera than the surrounding land.

On the other hand, the water at B appears jet black in the infrared photo, while the land around it is almost white. Thus the water in the pond absorbs more of the infrared rays than the land. The land also looks different in both photographs.

We have seen that the sun appears red at sunset because red light penetrates the haze and dust in the air better than other colors. Infrared waves penetrate even more than red light. Long-distance aerial photos are therefore generally taken with infrared cameras and film.

Another important use for infrared waves is shown in Fig. 70. When infrared waves are passed through a sample of a material, certain wave lengths are absorbed and others go through. An infrared spectroscope will show which wave lengths are absorbed and which are transmitted. Since each substance absorbs its own pattern of infrared waves, the spectroscope chart provides a quick way to analyze a material. In Fig. 70, sharp dips such as A and B reveal presence of cocaine in both materials.

Herschel's first experiment with infrared waves showed that they have more heating effect than visible light. Infrared waves, together with visible light, bombard the atoms and molecules of materials and cause them to move. It is this "molecular motion" that we observe as heat.

Molecular motion also causes infrared waves to be sent out. We say that a hot object radiates "heat." Actually it is not "heat" that is being radiated, but

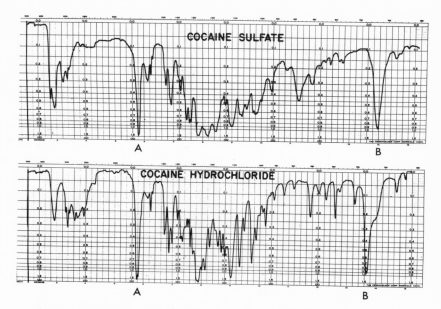

Fig. 70. An infrared spectrum can be used to make a chemical analysis of a material. The dips reveal which wave lengths have been absorbed. (Perkin Elmer Corp.)

infrared waves, or "heat-causing" waves. The intense heat in the sun causes infrared waves, visible light, and other forms of electromagnetic waves to be sent out. These waves all travel toward the earth at a speed of 186,000 miles a second. When the waves strike the earth, a portion of the radiation is absorbed, and the rest is reflected back into space. The portion that is absorbed warms the earth.

Most of the heating effect of the sun comes from infrared waves. Without them the earth would freeze and we would die.

Scientists have found ways to photograph the infrared radiation from hot objects. The car in Fig. 71 was photographed by means of the infrared waves which it emitted while it stood in direct sunlight.

White areas mean that a great deal of infrared radiation was sent out; black areas mean that little was sent out.

Was the motor running? It would seem so. Look how hot (white) the hood is. Such infrared photos are very useful in analyzing the hot and cold parts of machines and buildings.

Fig. 71. This picture was taken by infrared light radiating from the automobile. The white parts generate the most heat. (Barnes Engineering Co.)

There are many practical uses for infrared waves. For example, Fig. 72 shows a steelworker grilling a cheese sandwich with infrared rays from a white-hot furnace. Our "infrared" broilers work in the same manner. A coil of wire is heated electrically until it becomes red hot, then the infrared rays from the hot coil can be used to broil a steak. A similar process is used in industry for quickly drying paints and other liquid materials.

Fig. 72. This worker in a steel mill has his own infrared broiler. (United States Steel Corp.)

ULTRAVIOLET LIGHT

Have you ever been sunburned? If so, you can blame it on ultraviolet rays. This kind of radiation, found beyond the violet end of a spectrum (Fig. 49), is quite destructive. In fact, if most of the sun's ultraviolet rays were not stopped by the atmosphere, we would soon be killed by direct exposure to them. In the early summer even a few hours' exposure to the weak ultraviolet rays that reach the ground is enough to give you a bad sunburn. Later in the summer a dark suntan will protect you from these rays.

Housewives hang clothes to dry in the sunlight to make use of the *germicidal* (germ-killing) power of ultraviolet radiation. Special ultraviolet lamps are used in hospital operating rooms to kill harmful germs. Such an ultraviolet lamp is on the inside rim of the overhead fixture in Fig. 73.

A moderate amount of exposure to ultraviolet rays is healthful. It helps create the vitamin D we need to make our bones grow strong. Doctors advise mothers to expose their children to some sunlight. Special sunlamps that produce ultraviolet rays are also used to tan the skin and produce vitamin D. Sunlamps must be used with care because an overexposure to their ultraviolet rays can cause severe sunburn and injury to the eyes.

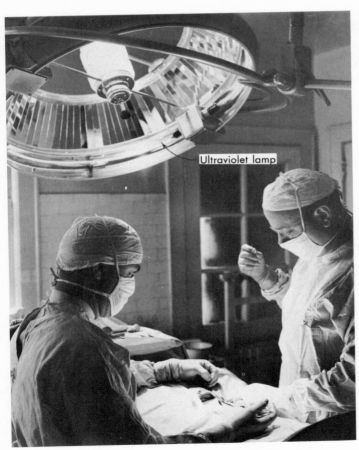

Ultraviolet lamp

Fig. 73. Hospital operating rooms use ultraviolet lamps to help kill germs. (Westinghouse Photo)

Ultraviolet radiation has widespread use in stage and sign lighting. Certain materials are *fluorescent* and glow brightly when illuminated with ultraviolet rays. These materials change some of the energy of the invisible high-frequency ultraviolet waves into lower-frequency visible light. Costumes and scenery painted with such fluorescent materials will glow brightly in ultraviolet radiation. If a lamp produces only ultraviolet rays and no visible light, the costumes and scenery on a stage can be made to glow brilliantly in the dark. The term *black light* is used to describe this effect.

Fluorescent markings on the instrument dials of airplanes are often illuminated by "black light" lamps. Illumination from ordinary light would interfere with the pilot's vision at night.

You have seen brilliantly colored posters and billboards in which the color stands out in sharp contrast to the surroundings. Fluorescent materials are added to the inks used to print these bright colors. When high-frequency violet and ultraviolet radiation in sunlight strikes the fluorescent materials, they are changed into lower-frequency red, yellow, and green light. The additional light thus produces a brighter color.

You are familiar with "fluorescent" lamps. Why is this name used? If you were to see a lighted lamp of this type which had a clear glass tube instead of the regular white one, it would appear bluish-green and rather dim. A large amount of the light given off by such lamps is invisible ultraviolet radiation that is normally wasted for illumination purposes.

But by coating the inside of the lamp tube with fluorescent powders, some of the wasted energy of the ultraviolet radiation is changed into visible light and the lamp appears much brighter.

Another interesting use of fluorescence is shown in Fig. 74. When viewed under ultraviolet rays, an old egg appears purple and a fresh egg appears scarlet. Chemical changes cause the eggshell of the old egg to fluoresce differently from that of the fresh egg. Doctors use a similar procedure to identify certain types of skin infections.

Fig. 75 shows how ultraviolet radiation may be used to locate and study a leak in a tank. A fluorescent liquid was permitted to run along the inside edges of the tank. When examined on the outside

Fig. 74. The old eggs give off a purple fluorescence under ultraviolet light and fresh eggs glow with a scarlet color. (Westinghouse Photo)

Fig. 75. A leak in a tank is revealed by a fluorescent glow. (Westinghouse Photo)

with an ultraviolet lamp, the location and length of the leak show up as the liquid fluoresces in the ultraviolet radiation.

INFRARED PROBLEM

Look at the automobile in Fig. 71. Can you answer these questions? (Remember, white areas in this photo mean high infrared radiation and probably a higher temperature.)

a. Why do the chromium strips and hubcaps appear dark?
b. Why is the ground under and in back of the car warmer than it is in front of the car?
c. Why are the tires warmer than the metal body?
d. The car is actually standing in bright sunlight. We would therefore expect infrared rays to be coming from the hot top of the car. Why is the top of the car dark?

Now turn to page 154 for the answers.

9
Extending the Spectrum

WE have said that light is a wave. But a wave of what? A water wave moves in water. A sound wave moves in air or other materials. But in what does a light wave move?

In 1863 the English scientist James Clerk Maxwell suggested that light was composed of "electromagnetic waves" caused by electrical particles vibrating inside a material.

You can begin to understand what this means by doing a simple experiment with a magnet.

Place a magnet on a table and cover it with a sheet of paper. Gently sprinkle iron filings (bits of iron) onto the paper. An interesting pattern of *lines of force* will form around the magnet (Fig. 76). The pattern is called a *magnetic field*.

In your experiment the lines of force do not move. But if you made an *electromagnet* and sent a *changing electric current* through it, the lines of force would move in time to the changes. In fact there would be two groups of moving lines, one for magnetic lines of force and the other for electrical lines of force.

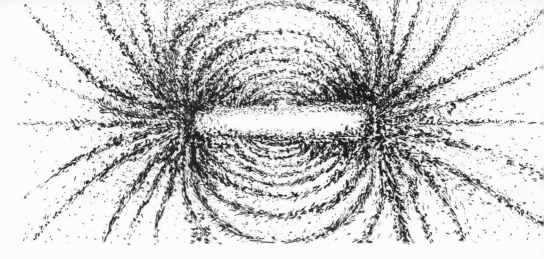

Fig. 76. A pattern of "lines of force" forms a "magnetic field" around a magnet.

Maxwell believed that a light wave was composed of both sets of lines of force moving at a speed of 186,000 miles a second. A light wave was, therefore, an *electromagnetic* wave.

According to Maxwell, an electrical particle moving rapidly back and forth could cause an electromagnetic wave. If the rate of vibration was great enough, visible light waves would be sent out. High rates of vibrations would cause high-frequency violet and ultraviolet waves, while less-rapid vibrations would cause lower-frequency red and infrared waves.

Maxwell thought that it was possible to make electromagnetic waves with *any* rapidly vibrating electric current. In 1878 the German scientist Heinrich Hertz proved that Maxwell was right. Hertz made an electromagnetic wave by producing a rapidly vibrating electric current. It was the first *radio wave*—brother to a light wave. He transmitted radio waves across a room to create tiny sparks. Hertz's experiment was further evidence that light waves

112

and radio waves are electromagnetic waves.

How does a radio station create radio waves? The basic idea is simple. A powerful, rapidly vibrating electric current is sent up and down an aerial. One station may send a million surges of electrical particles up and down the aerial in one second, creating an electromagnetic wave with a *frequency* of one million vibrations per second. The wave travels outward, hits the aerial of your radio, and creates a million electrical vibrations per second in your set. The tubes and other parts of the set then change the pattern of electrical vibrations into sound.

Another station might use a frequency of 1,200,000 vibrations per second; still another 650,000. You tune in a station according to the frequency of its electromagnetic wave. The number 120 on the dial of a radio might represent a station with a frequency of 1,200,000 waves per second; the number 65, a station with a frequency of 650,000 waves per second. Television waves are the same kind of electromagnetic waves except that their frequency is much higher, about 100 million per second.

Scientists can make similar waves with frequencies of over a billion times a second. If you send such waves through a person, they cause heat, resulting in an artificial fever. Doctors use these waves in heat treatments known as *diathermy*. The waves used in diathermy approach the frequency of infrared waves and begin to act like them.

Fig. 77 provides additional evidence that radio and light waves are similar. The aerial in the photo is part of a radar transmitter that bounces radio waves

off the moon. The wave comes back from the moon in about 2½ seconds. Since scientists know the distance to the moon, it is easy for them to calculate that the radio wave travels at the same speed as a light wave—186,000 miles per second.

Maxwell's theory that electromagnetic waves are caused by vibrating electrical particles works nicely for radio waves which have a very low frequency as compared with visible light. But as an explanation of visible-light waves, the theory has serious flaws. Scientists therefore needed to find another theory to explain how light is caused inside atoms.

In Chapter 7 we described how Niels Bohr pictured light as caused by an electron jumping from an outer orbit in an atom to an inner one. The evidence for the Bohr theory was so overwhelming that it has become the accepted explanation of the way in which light is produced.

Of course, this new picture brings with it many mysteries. Why should an electron jumping from one orbit to another cause an electromagnetic wave? Why are there only certain orbits? Why isn't any orbit possible? No one knows. These mysteries remain to be solved in the future.

Now, let us return to Fig. 49. The numbers on the left-hand side of the chart represent the frequencies of the waves. The chart starts at a frequency of about 10,000 waves per second and increases by multiples of ten all the way up to 10 sextillion. Fig. 49 is a gigantic spectrum of electromagnetic waves, far larger than our original visible-light spectrum.

Radio waves start at about 10,000 waves per second and go up to the regular broadcast waves (about 1 million per second), into radar and experimental frequencies (10 billion per second). At about 100 billion per second we reach infrared waves. The waves most useful for heating are at frequencies of about 100 trillion per second. At about 500 trillion per second the visible-light region is reached. The quadrillion mark brings us into ultraviolet, the sunburn and germ-killing waves.

X RAYS

As we approach 100 quadrillion waves per second, the ultraviolet shades into a new kind of wave—the X ray. How were X rays discovered?

In 1895, the German scientist Wilhelm Roentgen was experimenting with electric current. When he sent a current through a tube containing a gas at low pressure, he noticed that minerals nearby developed a fluorescent glow in the dark. This occurred even when the tube was completely enclosed in a box. Some kind of mysterious "rays" were coming through the solid box! These penetrating rays became known as *X rays*. Upon further study X rays were found to be electromagnetic waves of a higher frequency than ultraviolet waves. The frequencies of ultraviolet waves were about a million billion per second, those of X rays about a billion billion (a quintillion) per second!

In Fig. 9 we saw that ordinary light can pass through human flesh. But X rays are far more penetrating than ordinary light. Fig. 78A is a photograph of a painting. Fig. 78B is an X-ray photograph of part of the same painting. The X-ray picture penetrates the opaque paint and reveals another picture underneath.

When the frequency of the X ray is stepped up, its penetrating power increases. With powerful X rays we can look right through the human body and

Fig. 78. X rays uncover a hidden painting. (General Electric Co.)

see detail in the bones (Fig. 79). X rays are of great importance not only in medicine but also in industry, where they are used to detect weak spots in metal parts. Notice how clearly the X-ray photo in Fig. 79 shows the working parts of the electric shaver through its outer case.

How are X rays produced? An electric current is a stream of electrons. If we shoot electrons through a vacuum tube and let them hit a piece of metal, X rays will come out of the metal. If we use a higher voltage (electrical force), the speed of the electrons increases. The greater speed causes a higher impact, which in turn results in a higher frequency and more penetrating rays. A dentist uses about 15,000 volts when he X-rays your teeth. But to detect holes in solid metal, an engineer might use 250,000 volts, or even a million volts.

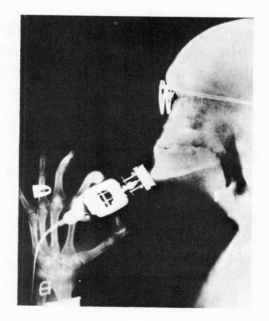

Fig. 79. The inner parts of the human body and the electric shaver are revealed by X rays. (Westinghouse Photo)

We speak of "soft" and "hard" X rays. Soft X rays are the lower-frequency rays that penetrate only soft objects like flesh. Higher-frequency hard X rays can penetrate solid objects of some thickness. Hard X rays begin to resemble another kind of radiation known as *gamma rays*.

GAMMA AND COSMIC RAYS

How did we first learn about gamma rays? They were discovered quite by accident by the French scientist Henri Becquerel in 1896 as he was experimenting with light.

You have seen luminous materials that glow in the dark. These materials are either *phosphorescent* or *radioactive*. A phosphorescent material must first be exposed to light before it will glow. The electrons in a phosphorescent material capture and store the light energy. Fig. 80 shows how they do this by jumping to "higher-energy" orbits a bit further from the nucleus of the atom. When the light is removed, the electrons jump back to their normal positions and give out the light energy that they have stored. Gradually, as the electrons jump back into place, the light becomes dimmer and finally disappears.

Becquerel was trying to find out if uranium ore was phosphorescent. One day he happened to put a piece of uranium ore on some photographic paper which was wrapped in thick black paper. Then, perhaps forgetting whether the photographic paper had been used, he developed it. He found that the

118

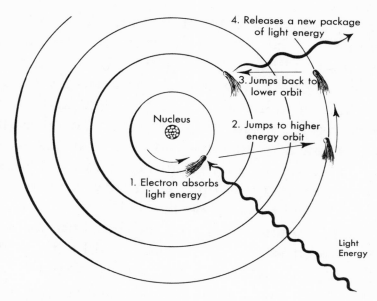

Fig. 80. Phosphorescent objects glow in the dark because electrons jump to a higher-energy orbit when they absorb light energy, but later jump back to send out splashes of light energy.

photographic paper under the uranium ore had blackened right through its wrapping. Becquerel had discovered a new type of luminous mineral. He didn't know it at the time, but he had also discovered atomic energy.

The uranium ore was *radioactive.* It contained a material which gave off very-high-frequency rays that were more penetrating than ordinary X rays. They are now known as *gamma rays.* It was also found that uranium ore gave off high-speed atomic bullets as well as gamma rays. The French scientists Pierre and Marie Curie analyzed the uranium ore to find out what was causing the rays and atomic bullets. They discovered *radium.* Radium was such

119

a powerful source of energy in the form of penetrating rays and atomic bullets that scientists were astounded. They had been given the first glimpse of atomic energy.

Tiny amounts of radioactive materials are used on luminous watch dials to create light. Radioactive atoms explode and shoot out high-speed atomic bullets and rays. Electrons in nearby atoms are hit by these atomic bullets and rays and are knocked into higher-energy orbits. Then they jump back to create the light we see on the dial.

Unlike luminous materials of the phosphorescent type, which require exposure to light, the radioactive light sources are self-luminous. They continue to glow year after year with slight loss of power.

Since Becquerel's time, scientists have found many ways to create gamma rays artificially. They usually do this by shooting parts of atoms at materials. As an atom is struck, it may break apart and release new high-speed atomic pieces plus penetrating gamma rays.

This process goes on all the time in nature. For example, Fig. 81 shows what happens when a polished piece of uranium ore is placed on film. The white spots are the areas that contain radioactive material and give off gamma rays plus atomic bullets.

High-speed atomic bullets and penetrating gamma rays are constantly raining down upon us from outer space. If you listen to a Geiger counter you will hear occasional clicks, even though there is no radioactive ore nearby. Each click represents the passage of a gamma ray or atomic bullet through the tube of the Geiger counter. Large numbers of atomic bullets and rays go through our bodies every second. They probably effect our lives more than we realize.

The energy of gamma rays and atomic bullets is measured in millions of *electron-volts*. This type of radiation can be produced by smashing high-speed particles, such as electrons, into an object. Electrical forces amounting to millions of volts are used to speed up the electrons. But the energy of some of the radiation coming from outer space is measured

Fig. 81. Gamma rays plus particles from splitting atoms produced this picture when a film was placed next to a piece of polished uranium ore. (General Electric Co.)

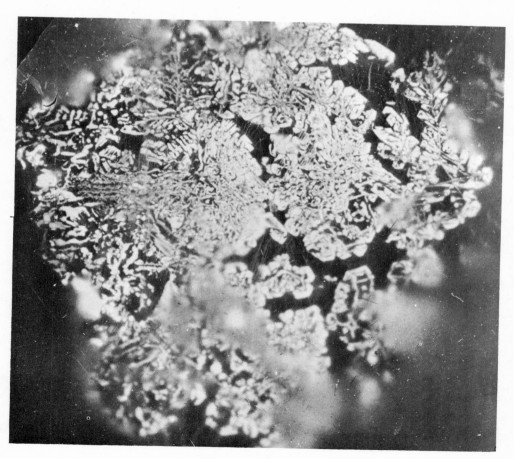

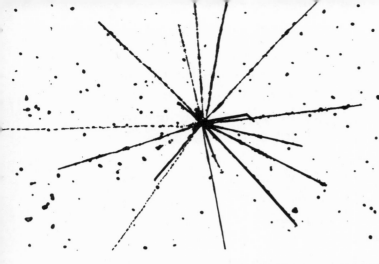

Fig. 82. This picture reveals the smashup of an atom as a result of cosmic rays. (Brookhaven National Lab.)

in billions or even billions of billions of electron-volts. Radiation from outer space is therefore far more penetrating and damaging than that from ordinary gamma rays. We call the atomic bullets and rays from outer space *cosmic rays*. The frequencies of cosmic rays are measured in sextillions (billions of trillions) of waves per second.

Scientists have built machines that will duplicate cosmic rays. Fig. 82 is a photograph of the explosion of an atom set off by a man-made cosmic ray. The straight lines forming the star pattern are caused by the rapidly moving parts of the smashed atom.

Scientists hope to unlock more secrets of the atom by such studies. All of us sincerely hope that mankind will find a way to put this knowledge to peaceful use.

WAVES OR PARTICLES?

As scientists explored the enlarged spectrum that started with visible light, an interesting mystery began to develop. You will recall that Newton's idea

122

of light bullets lost favor in the nineteenth century because the wave theory explained refraction, interference, and polarization. Finally the bullet theory was thrown out completely. It did not seem to work at all.

But you may have noticed that as we progressed to higher frequencies, from visible and radio waves to infrared, ultraviolet, and X rays, we began to use the word "rays" rather than "waves." We speak of radio waves, not radio rays; but we say "cosmic rays," not cosmic waves. The term "cosmic rays" includes not only electromagnetic waves but also a wide assortment of bullets composed of speeding atomic particles.

As frequencies increase, the "waves" begin to act more and more like destructive bullets, and less and less like waves. When a high-frequency electromagnetic wave (cosmic ray) hits an atom, it seems to concentrate all its energy in one spot and smash the atom to bits. A wave is more spread out than a particle. And even if it had more energy, it is difficult to see how a wave could penetrate into a single atom without affecting many atoms nearby. But it does. So scientists now think of light energy as coming in packages called *photons*. Perhaps the photons are little bundles of wave energy somewhat like the wiggly wave groups in Fig. 83.

In dealing with low-frequency and low-energy radio waves, we can explain most of the actions we observe by forgetting about bulletlike photons and thinking only of electromagnetic waves. But as we go up the frequency scale toward ultraviolet, X rays,

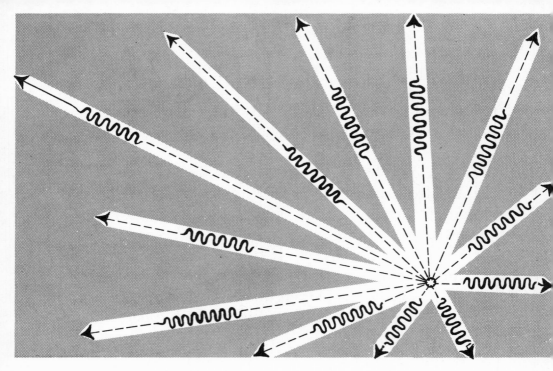

Fig. 83. Today we picture light as due to the motion of tiny bundles of wave motion called "photons."

gamma rays, and cosmic rays, the light energy acts more like bullets and we have to consider the idea of photons. This contradiction in the theories of light is the subject of intensive study by scientists. They hope to solve this mystery as they have solved so many others.

The many changes that have occurred in the theories of light in the past few hundred years demonstrate an important characteristic of science. As our knowledge grows and we solve more of the mysteries of nature, we discover an increasing number of new problems to solve. Each new theory helps us to understand a bit more about our world, yet at the same time raises new questions and problems. Thus the work of scientists will probably never come to an end.

124

PART III

Optics

Now let us turn from "invisible light" waves back to the ordinary light we know best. One of the main uses of visible light is to enable us to see. The science of optics is concerned with the improvement of vision by means of lenses, mirrors, and other devices. The most important part of each of these devices is the *lens*.

10 Lenses

THE "water strider," whose shadow appears on the stream bottom in Fig. 84, can teach us something about lenses.

The water strider can walk on water because it weighs so little and because the water has *surface tension.* Surface tension resembles an elastic film on top of the water.

Notice that the long body of the insect casts a shadow of about the same size. But the six thin legs seem to cast large oval shadows. Why? There is a bright rim around each shadow of a leg, but none around the shadow of the rest of the insect's body. Why does this bright rim occur?

We can find the explanation of this interesting effect by studying what happens when light passes through lens-shaped pieces of glass.

In Fig. 85, three parallel rays of light (A) are entering a *concave* (inward-curving) piece of glass (B). The concave lens bends the upper and lower rays (C and D) away from the center ray (E). The once-parallel rays now *diverge* (spread apart).

The diverging rays then strike a *convex* (outward-

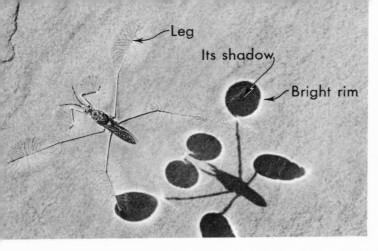

Leg

Its shadow

Bright rim

Fig. 84. Why do the shadows of the thin legs of the water insect look so large and black, while the shadow of the body looks normal? (H. Lou Gibson)

curving) lens (F). The convex lens bends the spreading rays so that they *converge* (come together) somewhere beyond G.

Why do lenses bend light as they do? Fig. 86 shows three rays of light striking a convex lens. The center section (A) resembles a rectangle with parallel sides. In Fig. 39 we saw that a ray of light striking a rectangular piece of glass at right angles passes through without changing its direction. Ray B therefore goes straight through the glass.

Fig. 85. This photograph of the passage of three light rays through two lenses reveals many interesting facts about light. (Bausch and Lomb Optical Co.)

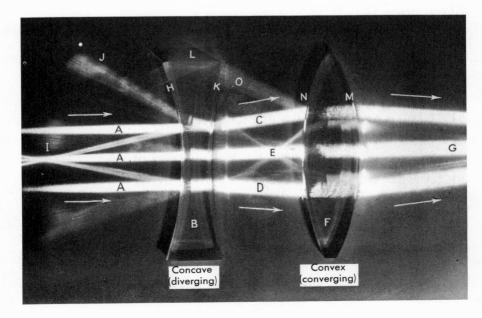

Concave (diverging)

Convex (converging)

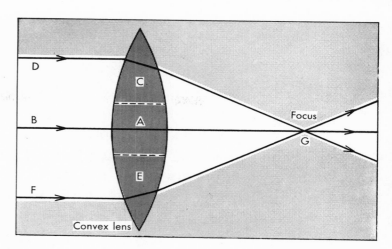

Fig. 86. A converging (convex) lens causes light rays to focus at a point.

The upper part of the lens (C) resembles a triangular prism and bends the light ray (D) that strikes it toward the wide part (base) of the prism, as in Fig. 33. The bottom part of the lens (E) is like an upside-down triangular prism, and bends ray F upward toward its base. The net result is that all three rays converge (come together) at point G. The convex lens is said to bring rays to a *focus* (G).

Now, let us look at the action of a concave lens (Fig. 87). Three parallel rays enter the glass. Ray B strikes the rectangular center section (A) and passes straight through. Ray C strikes the upside-down prism part of the lens (D) and bends toward the wide top of the lens. The third section of the lens (E) is a right-side-up prism, and ray F is bent to-

Fig. 87. A diverging (concave) lens causes rays of light to spread apart.

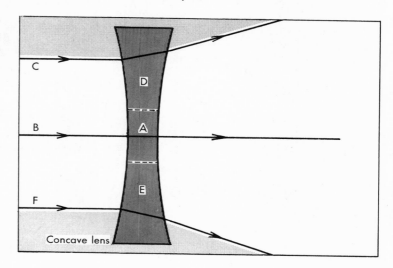

ward its base, at the bottom part of the lens. The net result is that the rays diverge (spread apart) when they leave the lens.

Convex lenses tend to bend light rays closer together; concave lenses tend to spread them apart.

But how does this explain the shadow of the water strider in Fig. 84. Although the water strider is very light, it weighs enough to indent the water under each leg, causing a small hollow in the surface of the water. In Fig. 88, the curve of the hollow in the water is shown to consist of a central concave part (A) and two convex parts (B and C). The concave part (A) spreads the rays away from the center part of the shadow at D. A large dark area is therefore seen at D. But the convex parts of the water at B and C make the rays converge and concentrate the light at E and F to create the bright rim around the dark area.

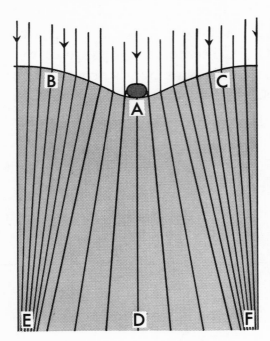

Fig. 88. The large, dark shadow of the insect's leg in Fig. 84 is caused by light rays diverging from the concave water surface at A. The bright rim is caused by converging light from the convex surfaces at B and C.

FORMING AN IMAGE

Convex lenses are used in optical instruments, such as cameras and telescopes, because they can form images. Fig. 89 shows a convex lens forming an image on a wall. A boy stood near a window. A convex lens was held up near a wall opposite the window and moved back and forth. When the lens was a certain distance from the wall, a clear upside-down image of the boy was formed on the wall. Try doing this yourself with a magnifying glass.

You can also observe an inverted image by holding a magnifying glass at arm's length, as in Fig. 90. A transparent glass marble or a jar of water will also form upside-down images.

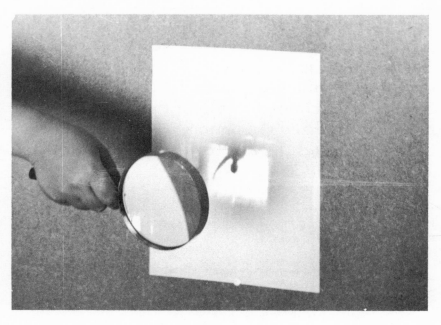

Fig. 89. A converging lens can produce an inverted image on a wall.

Fig. 90. A converging lens forms an inverted image when it is held at a distance from the eye.

A convex lens forms an image by causing rays to converge to a focus. Fig. 91 shows a group of light rays reflecting from a flower (A) toward a lens (B). As in Figs. 86 and 87, the ray striking the center of the lens goes almost straight through without any change in direction. The top of the lens bends the rays downward and the bottom tends to bend them upward. The rays therefore come together and focus at C.

If we put a screen at C, the point where the rays

Fig. 91. The ability of a lens to make light rays converge is the cause of formation of inverted images.

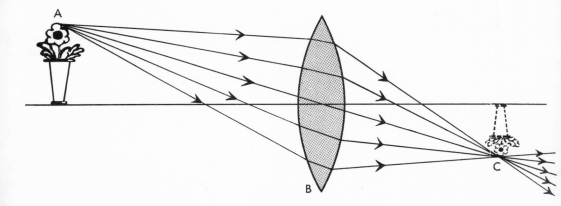

meet, a duplicate of the original source of light (the flower) appears on the screen. We call this duplicate an *image*.

Now suppose we move the screen closer to the lens where the rays of light have not yet met. Instead of a spot of light, we get a blurred area. The image is "out of focus." If we move the screen farther from the lens, the rays have already crossed and have begun to spread apart. Again, we see a blurred image. You can see why it was necessary to "focus an image" on the wall by moving the lens back and forth in the experiment in Fig. 89.

Notice that the rays in Fig. 91 start from A, above the center line of the lens, and end below that line. This causes the image to be *inverted* (upside-down).

It is easy to form an image that is larger or smaller than the original object. Try this experiment at night with a table lamp and a convex lens. Any magnifying glass is convex and can be used for this experiment. Remove the lampshade to expose the lighted bulb.

Bring the lens a few inches from the lamp bulb. A very large, inverted image of the bulb will appear on a nearby wall. Form images in this manner on different walls. You will notice that the farther away the wall is, the larger the image.

Now bring the lens near the wall and again focus an image of the lamp bulb on the wall. This time the image will be very small. Try this experiment on each wall in the room. You will notice that when the lens is farthest from the lamp, the image is smallest.

An image of any size, large or small, can easily be made with a convex lens by adjusting the distances from lens and lamp and lens and wall.

Why does this happen? Fig. 92A shows how an image is formed when the lens is far from the object. Notice how the rays meet rather close to the lens to form a small image. This is the way an image is formed by the lens of a camera. Your eye also forms images in this way.

Fig. 92B shows how an enlarged image is formed when the object is brought closer to the lens. A projector or a microscope forms images in this manner.

Fig. 92. A larger image is produced by bringing the object closer to the lens.

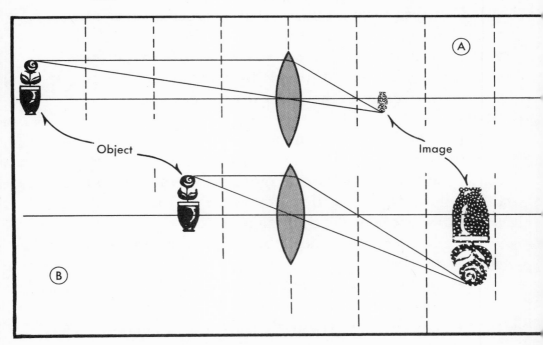

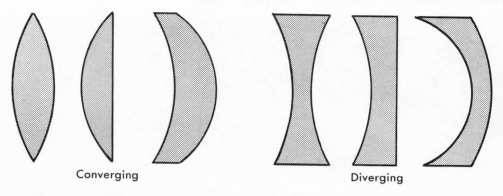

Converging

Diverging

Fig. 93. Converging (convex) lenses are thicker in the middle. Diverging (concave) lenses are thinner in the middle.

DIFFERENT LENSES

A lens may have one surface convex and the other concave, as shown in Fig. 93. Should we call it "convex" or "concave"? Would such a lens make rays of light *converge* (come together) or *diverge* (spread apart)? It all depends upon whether the lens is thicker in the middle or thinner. If it is thicker in the middle, it causes the rays to converge. Such a lens is therefore called *converging.* Most people call it *convex.*

If the lens is thinner in the middle than at the edges, it causes rays to diverge. Such a lens is called *diverging.* Most people call it *concave.* We have seen that a lens that is convex on both sides forms an inverted image (Fig. 90). All converging lenses do the same. On the other hand, it is impossible for diverging lenses to form images on a screen by themselves because they spread rays apart rather than bring them to a focus. However, you can see images by looking at an object through diverging lenses. Such images are erect (right side up) and small, as in Fig. 94.

135

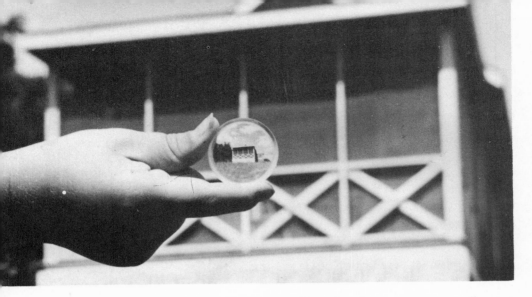

Fig. 94. When you look through a diverging lens you see a small, erect image.

Lenses also differ in *focal length.* Fig. 95 shows the way two converging lenses focus the same parallel rays (such as rays of sunlight). The curve of the glass in lens A is more convex than that of lens B. As a result, lens A bends light more sharply than B. The rays passing through lens A focus at point C close to the lens. The same rays passing through lens B focus farther away at D. Suppose that the rays converge four inches from lens A and eight inches from lens B. Then we say that lens A has a focal length of four inches and lens B has a focal length of eight inches.

The focal length of a lens determines how large an image of a particular object will be and how far from the lens it will form. Thus it is possible to design lenses to give larger or smaller images, as desired.

A cheap lens and an expensive one of the same focal length will form images of a given object that

136

are equal in size and distance from the lens. But they may differ in important details. The cheap lens may produce a blurred, distorted image with colored edges. The better lens will produce clearer, less-distorted images without the colored edges.

We frequently refer to lenses as "strong" or "weak." A strong lens bends rays more sharply than a weak one. The lens of short focal length in Fig. 95 is "stronger" than the lens of long focal length (B). However, the words "strong" and "weak" are often misleading. For example, in a telescope greater magnification is obtained with a "weak" lens of greater focal length. Yet we would be tempted to call such a lens "strong" because of its high magnification. It is better, therefore, to refer simply to the actual focal length.

Fig. 95. A "weak" lens has a long "focal length." A "strong" lens bends light rays more sharply and makes them focus closer to the lens.

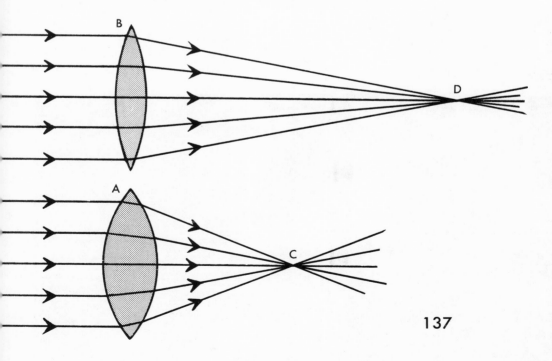

LENS DEFECTS

The simple kind of converging lens that we have been talking about is rarely used by itself in optical instruments of good quality. Fig. 96 shows one reason why. Notice that as the five rays of light strike the lens, they bend and come together. However, the rays that pass through the outer edges of the lens don't meet at the same point as the rays closer to the center. This causes a blurred and distorted image. The name given to this defect is *spherical aberration*. The word "aberration" means "defect." This particular defect is called "spherical aberration" because it arises from the spherical shape of the curve of the surfaces of simple lenses.

Spherical aberration is easily remedied by not using the outer edges of the lens. When only the area near the center of the lens is used, the light rays are focused sharply. But this improvement

Fig. 96. The lens defect, "spherical aberration," results from the fact that the outer and inner portions of a lens focus rays of light at different points. (Wide World)

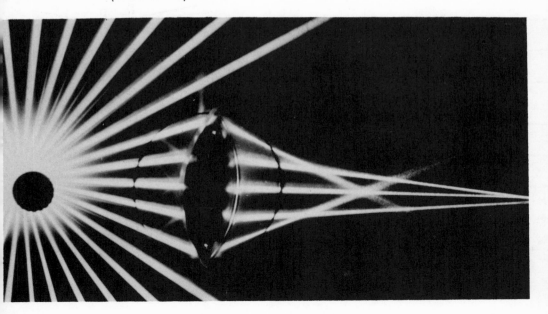

cuts down the size (diameter) of the lens. A large-diameter lens is often needed to admit more light energy. In fine optical instruments it is sometimes necessary to use lenses of special design to improve the image. Four or more lenses may be combined in one instrument. Lenses of this type often cost hundreds or even thousands of dollars.

If you look through a very cheap telescope or pair of field glasses you will see colored edges around all lines in the image. One side of the edge of a building may appear red, and the opposite side blue. We know that white light is composed of all colors of the spectrum. When white light passes through an ordinary lens, the red rays and the blue rays that come from the same place bend differently and therefore do not focus in the same place. This causes the defect of colored edges in the image, known as *chromatic aberration.* "Chromatic" means "color." An *achromatic* (color-corrected) lens combination brings the red and blue rays together to focus at the same point and produces an image without colored edges.

A third defect of lenses is shown in Fig. 85. Notice that the multiple reflections and refractions send rays of light off in many directions. This stray light causes undesirable bright spots in the image and makes it less sharp and clear. To reduce this defect quality lenses are *coated* with a thin layer of transparent material that cuts down the amount of light reflected from the lens surface.

LENS PROBLEM

Can you answer the following questions about Fig. 85?

    a. How can you prove that the rays of light come from the left and travel toward the right?

    b. Explain the focusing of rays at I.

    c. Explain the formation of the ray at J.

    d. What causes the converging rays at E?

    e. Explain the formation of rays at L.

Now turn to page 154 for the answers.

11 How We See

THE basic principles of sight may be understood by comparing the eye with the operation of a camera.

A lens at the front of the camera forms an upside-down image on a film at the back of the camera, just as the simple lens in Fig. 89 forms an image on the wall. Special chemicals on the film are affected by the light. An image of the original scene then appears on the film when it is developed.

A camera usually has several adjustments for taking pictures. The lens is often moved back and forth to focus images on the film for objects at different distances. There are adjustments for controlling the amount of light that enters the camera, and for taking pictures of rapidly moving objects in a shorter interval of time.

The eye is similar to a camera in many ways. It has a lens to form an image. It has controls for letting in more light when it is dark and less light when it is bright. And it has an adjustment for focusing an image.

When you look at an eye, you see a round colored

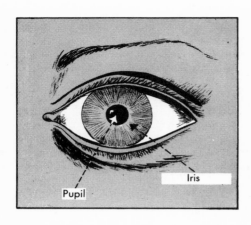

Iris

Fig. 97. The colored iris is a muscle that controls the amount of light entering the eye through the pupil.

circle on a white background (Fig. 97). At the center of the colored circle is a small black circle, called the *pupil.* Light enters the eye through the pupil, which appears black because you are looking into the dark inside part of the eye.

The colored part of the eye around the pupil is a circular muscle called the *iris.* Look at your pupil and iris in a mirror in a dimly lit room. The pupil (opening to the eye) is large. But then look at your eye in a mirror outdoors in the sun. The pupil shrinks and becomes very small.

The purpose of the muscle in the iris is to control the amount of light that enters the eye. Too much light causes harm and too little results in a dim image. The iris reacts to changes in the amount of light and opens or closes accordingly.

Fig. 98 is a simplified diagram of the inside of the eye. The front of the eyeball is covered with a transparent protecting tissue called the *cornea.* Behind it is the iris. A convex lens of transparent material is located behind the retina. This lens focuses rays of light to form an image on the back of the eyeball.

The back of the eye contains many tiny nerves.

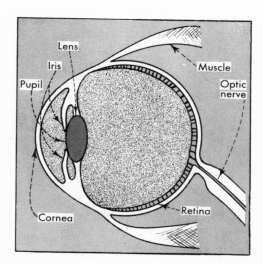

Fig. 98. A convex lens in the eye forms an image on the retina.

Each nerve is like an electric wire. It carries an electric current to the brain whenever it is struck by light. The brain then puts these electric messages together to tell you what kind of object you are looking at.

We know that a converging lens produces an upside-down image. So does the lens of the eye. Then why don't we see things upside-down?

When a baby is born, it does not see people, houses, animals, and toys. It merely sees moving colored lights and darks. The baby must learn to see, just as it must learn to walk. It learns by experience that a certain pattern of light means a person; another pattern means a dog; and still others mean houses or trees. Messages from certain nerves mean "up." Messages from other nerves mean "down." It is the pattern of electric messages that counts, and you learn to recognize patterns of lights and darks by experience.

You will understand this better if you have ever used a microscope, which produces an upside-down image. The first time you look through the micro-

143

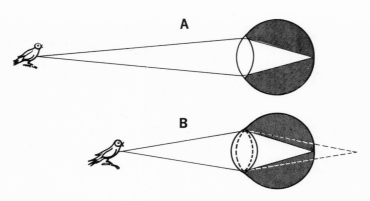

Fig. 99. The lens of the eye automatically adjusts itself to keep images in focus on the retina.

scope, at a small moving animal, you become confused. When you try to move the slide to follow the animal, it moves the wrong way! But with a bit of practice you soon adjust to the upside-down motion. After a while, you move the slide correctly without thinking about it. It has become automatic.

The camera has an adjustment to focus objects for different distances. The eye has such an adjustment too. When you look at something far away, the lens is usually just right for proper focusing (Fig. 99A). If the object is brought closer, the rays no longer meet on the retina and the image appears blurred (dotted lines in Fig. 99B). But a muscle near the lens of the eye corrects this by making the lens bulge a bit (become more convex). This bends the rays more sharply, and they come to a focus once again. This process is called *accommodation* and is pictured in Fig. 99B. Notice how the lens becomes thicker (more convex) in order to focus the rays more sharply.

However, there is a limit to this process. Close one eye and look at your finger, held as far away as possible. Slowly bring your finger closer to the eye. It is clearly visible until it is about ten inches from

144

the eye. If the finger approaches much closer, it begins to appear blurred. You can feel the strain of the muscle inside the eye as it tries to keep the image in focus.

WEARING GLASSES

Why do people wear eyeglasses? You would probably answer, "To see better." Of course, that is true. But why do glasses enable some people to see better?

All the muscles in the body become weaker with age, and the eye muscles are no exception. As a person ages, the muscles that adjust the shapes of his eye lenses become weaker. They can no longer accommodate for a ten-inch distance (Fig. 100A). The best the eye muscles can then do is to accommodate for a distance of perhaps twenty inches from the eye. But when one must hold a book that far away to avoid blurring, the image of the print on the retina is very small, and therefore hard to read.

Such a person is *farsighted*, because he sees objects clearly only when they are farther away than the normal ten inches. The farsighted person is unable to thicken his eye lenses enough to bring rays from a nearby object to a focus. He therefore must use converging (thicker in the middle) lenses to assist his eye lenses in bending light rays to a focus on the retina (Fig. 100B).

An older person may find that distant objects look blurred when he looks at them through his reading glasses. He then removes them for distant vision. Or he may wear *bifocals,* in which lenses of different

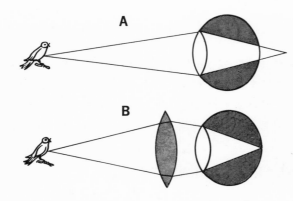

Fig. 100. Images of nearby objects are out of focus for "far-sighted" people. Eyeglasses with converging lenses bend the light rays to bring the images to a focus on the retina.

focal length are set into the lower part of the glasses. To see distant objects, he looks through the upper part of the glasses. To see near objects, he looks through the lower part. Many older people use two pairs of glasses, one for near vision and one for far.

Some young people are also farsighted. The oval shape of the eyes shown in Fig. 100 would be one cause of this defect in a young person.

Nearsighted people can see objects clearly only when the objects are close to their eyes. The trouble here is caused either by the shape of the eyeballs or by a defect in the lenses which causes the rays to come to a focus and form an image in front of the retina rather than right on it (Fig. 101A). You

Fig. 101. When a nearsighted person views a distant object, the rays of light form before the retina. Eyeglasses with diverging lenses spread the rays apart to focus the images on the retina.

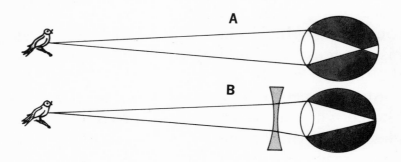

might think of the nearsighted eye lens as being too "strong," it bends the rays too sharply. In that case, the use of a diverging lens spreads the rays outward a bit, and thus helps the eye to form a clear image on the retina, as in Fig. 101B.

OPTICAL INSTRUMENTS

A number of optical instruments have been invented which assist our sight in various ways. For example, a *magnifying glass* can produce greatly enlarged images of small objects. It is simply a converging lens held between the object and the eye.

How does it magnify? Fig. 102 shows one ray of light coming from the head (A) of an insect. The ray is bent downward by the lens toward B and enters the eye. Another ray of light (C) goes straight through the center of the lens and also enters the eye. Your brain interprets both rays as coming from D, a point that is much higher than the original head of the insect. As a result the insect appears to be larger than it actually is.

A *telescope* is basically a lens of long focal length. Such a lens forms a large image. The greater the focal length, the larger the image. Long barrels or

Fig. 102. The illusion of a magnified object is caused by the way in which a convex lens bends light rays.

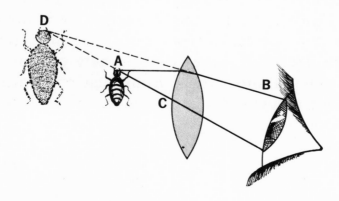

tubes are therefore needed for telescopes. An eyepiece, a kind of magnifying glass, is then used to examine the large image formed by the front lens (objective) and to provide further magnification.

Astronomers prefer to photograph the enlarged image and study it at leisure. The enlarged image formed by the objective is photographed directly without the use of an eyepiece.

A *projector,* or an *enlarger,* contains a lens held near a slide or picture. An enlarged image is formed on a distant screen in much the same manner as pictured in Fig. 92B. A large part of the expense of a projector is caused by the need for a strong concentrated light source to produce a bright image. Special bulbs, lenses, mirrors, and other parts are required for this purpose.

The *microscope* greatly resembles the projector, in that a lens is brought close to the object to produce a distant enlarged image. However, instead of projecting this image upon a screen, it is usually examined with a magnifying *eyepiece.* In the *microprojector* the eyepiece is eliminated and the image is projected directly onto a screen.

We have come to the end of our book. But it should be clear to you that this is by no means the end of the story of light. Each year, as scientists add to their knowledge and probe deeper into the mysteries of the nature of light, they find more and more that remains unknown. And as they continue their never-ending search, the new products and new industries that result from their researches help to make our world a better and happier place.

Answers to Problems

PAGE 24, SCREEN PROBLEM

Light travels in straight lines. Some of the light rays traveling toward your eye are blocked by the metal wires of the first screen. But other rays get through. Of those rays that get through, some are then blocked by the wires of the second screen while other rays get through. As we look at the screens we see some areas where light goes straight through both screens, and other areas where light is blocked by one of the screens. Thus, some areas appear dark and others do not. Since the wires of the screens have the same spacing, this blocking occurs in a large region. But because one screen is closer to us than the other, the angles to our eyes are different, and therefore a dark area changes to a light one as we look in different places.

The actual pattern of the light and dark areas is determined by the spacings of the wires, the angles between the screens and our eyes, and the distance of the screens from us.

PAGE 50, MIRROR PROBLEM 1

a. The windows below the scaffold reflect light from a newspaper and rope on the ground. The reflection of the ground seems to be just below the first-floor window. Therefore the painters are probably at the second story.

b. The image of the ground in the windows shows a pattern of bricks or blocks. No curbs, cars, or people are seen. The evidence seems to point to a courtyard rather than a street, but we can't be sure.

c. The shadow of the painter on the right is rather short. The sun is therefore high in the sky and the time is probably closer to noon than early morning or late afternoon.

d. Note the small stickers on each windowpane. New windows come with such stickers. In addition, if the building were occupied it is likely that lights would be on and we would then be able to see objects inside. The building is probably new.

e. Notice the blurred hand of the painter on the right. The hand would appear blurred in a photograph only if it were moving; therefore the scaffold is being moved.

f. Since the picture "looks down" upon the ledge of the third-floor window at A, the camera and photographer are probably at the fourth-floor level.

PAGE 50, MIRROR PROBLEM 2

Light rays can bounce off one mirror or the other to form two images of the object standing between the mirrors. But it is also possible for light to bounce off the mirror on the left to the mirror on the right, and finally to your eye. This forms a third image. A fourth image is produced if light bounces off the mirror on the right, then the mirror on the left, and finally travels to the eye. Two more images are formed by triple reflections. The seventh image is formed by four-times reflections.

PAGE 65, REFRACTION PROBLEM 1

As the metal ball moves through the air it pushes the air in front of it out of the way. The faster it goes, the harder it pushes. A squeezed (compressed) region of air therefore exists in front of the ball. Squeezing changes the nature of the air a bit, and causes it to become denser (heavier). Light bends as it passes across the boundary between regular air and the compressed air. The dark and light lines in the photograph show where the refraction of light occurs. We then clearly see the "shock wave" caused by high speed of the ball.

How was the picture taken?

The photographer placed a special lamp on one side of the moving ball and the camera on the other side. As the ball passed by at a speed of 10,000 miles per hour, it triggered a mechanism that set off a pulse of light lasting only one ten-millionth of a second. The light rays from the lamp refract where the air is compressed by the moving ball and therefore bend away from the camera. These regions of compressed air show up as dark lines to reveal the position of the shock wave caused by the rapid motion of the ball.

PAGE 66, REFRACTION PROBLEM 2

Light travels in straight lines if it remains in one material, but as soon as light rays reach a different material they change direction. There is always some reflection at the surface of the new material. If the material is transparent, there is also a change of direction caused by refraction. The disturbance of the straight path of the light rays and the resulting change in direction make the object visible in air. A jar of water surrounded by air becomes visible because it disturbs the light rays that strike it.

Similarly, light rays moving under water travel in straight paths if no other material gets in the way. But if the rays strike an air bubble, reflections and refractions take place at the surface. We then see the disturbed rays of light and the bubble becomes visible. The air bubble under water looks very much like a drop of water in the air. The image of the girl is undistorted in this underwater picture because she and the camera are both immersed in the same transparent material (water) and the light is traveling straight from her to the camera.

PAGE 80, ILLUSION PROBLEM

Light is slowed down by different amounts as it passes through different kinds of transparent materials. The amount of bending is different for each material. A ray of light is bent more if it enters glass than if it enters water at an equal angle. The same ray entering a diamond at an equal angle would be bent even more because the light wave would be slowed down still further.

Each transparent material has a certain "index of refraction"—a measure of how much a light wave is slowed down and bent. For example, the index of refraction for water is 1.33. For a diamond it is 2.41. The higher the index of refraction, the more a light beam bends. Whenever two transparent materials with a different index of refraction are in contact, the light rays will always change speed and thus refract and reflect as they pass from one material to the other.

151

But what happens if the speed of light is *exactly* the same in two materials? The index of refraction is then the same for both. No bending of light occurs and there are no reflections. The light rays go right through without any change, just as though only one material were present. In Fig. 57 the glass tube that disappears is made of "pyrex" glass which has almost exactly the same index of refraction as the liquid (trichloroethylene) in the jar. It therefore disappears in the liquid.

The other tube is made of "soft" glass, which has a different index of refraction. It therefore refracts and reflects light, which then reaches our eyes to make the glass visible.

PAGE 97, COLOR PROBLEM

A yellow glass permits most of the red, orange, yellow, and green rays of the spectrum to pass through, but stops most of the blue and violet rays. Thus, blue light from the blue sky is reduced by the filter. This makes the sky appear darker in the second photograph.

On the other hand, the water droplets in the cloud reflect all colors equally well. Therefore the clouds appear white in both photos. The contrast between the white cloud and the dark sky makes the clouds stand out more sharply in the photo taken with the filter. That is why it was used.

a. Sharp, bright shadows are cast by the sun in Fig. 65B, but not in 65A. Therefore picture A was taken at a time when the ground was in the shadow of a cloud.

b. The greater blurring of the vanes of the windmill in photo B might indicate that the wind increased in speed.

c. Very little shift in the direction of the wind occurred, as shown by the positions of the vanes on the windmill in both A and B.

d. The lumpy *cumulus* clouds are characteristic of fair weather, usually with cool, not-too-humid air. Air that has been warmed by the ground rises until it becomes cold enough to condense and form cumulus clouds. Since the clouds seem to be low, the air is not too dry.

e. In Fig. 65B, the shadow of the small platform just below the rotating blades indicates that the sun is low in the sky. Is it morning or afternoon? As cumulus clouds of the type seen in the photo tend to develop in midday or afternoon, the photograph was probably taken in the late afternoon.

f. The way in which the water tank in the lower right-hand corner is illuminated indicates that the sun is to the right of the camera. Since the afternoon sun would be in the southwest, the camera is probably facing in a southeast direction, at right angles to the sun.

g. The vanes of the windmill show the wind to be coming from slightly behind and to the right of the camera. The wind is therefore from the west or southwest. Since the clouds are nearer to the camera in photo B, it was probably taken first. The west wind then pushed them farther away to produce the picture in A.

h. The clouds seem to be moving more in the direction in which the camera points than in the direction the vanes point. Wind directions on the ground often differ from wind directions above.

i. The clouds moved a bit and changed somewhat, but they are still almost the same in both pictures. Therefore the photos were probably taken a few minutes apart.

j. The streamerlike *cirrus* clouds in the lower left-hand corner are in almost exactly the same position in both photographs. They are therefore a greater distance away or are not moving. Since the wind is blowing, it is not likely that they would be still; they are probably farther away and also higher than the cumulus clouds.

k. Both photos show identical objects in exactly the same positions, so the camera was not moved.

PAGE 98, SPECTRUM PROBLEM

Astronomers explain the regular splitting and coming together of a star's spectrum lines by assuming that it is a *binary* (double) star. One star revolves about the other like two boxers circling each other. If the stars are equal in mass (weight), they will revolve around the point halfway between them.

Suppose that we see their orbits edgewise. And suppose that the star on the left is coming toward us. Then at that same moment the star on the right will be moving away from us. And at that very moment the spectrum lines for the approaching star will be shifted toward the violet, while the lines for the other star are shifted toward the red. Thus, we see a double set of spectrum lines, one set for each star.

As the two stars revolve, the one approaching us will, at a later time, be moving away, and the other will be moving toward us. At times when both stars are in a direct line with us, they will be moving sideward and no shift will occur in the spectrum lines. We then see the double spectrum lines come together. This happens periodically as the stars revolve about each other.

By observing the changing positions of the lines in the spectrum, an astronomer can accurately measure the time of revolution of the two stars. He can estimate the speed of each star from the amount of shift. By applying the mathematics of orbits he can then obtain information about the diameter of the orbit and the masses of both stars. All this from a simple splitting of spectrum lines!

PAGE 109, INFRARED PROBLEM

a. Shiny, white, smooth surfaces emit (give out) less infrared radiation than dark surfaces; therefore the chromium parts appear dark.

b. The engine is running. Hot exhaust from the engine runs through a pipe the full length of the underside of the car. In addition, a fan blows hot air from the radiator down under and to the rear of the car. This hot air spreads out sideward and warms the ground at the rear and to the sides of the car. This warming is greater than the heating caused by the sunlight in front of and beyond the car. Notice the hot streak caused by the hot exhaust gases behind the car.

c. If the car has been moving, friction with the ground has warmed the tires. If the tires were exposed to direct sunlight just before the picture was taken, they would have absorbed even more heat radiation because of their deep black color and rough surface. In addition, black objects radiate infrared rays more readily than shiny white surfaces.

d. It seems strange that the top, which is in direct sunlight, appears dark. It should heat up in the sun. But remember that the top of the car faces upward and most of the radiation travels in that direction to the cool air above. Very little radiation travels sideward toward the infrared camera. The top of the car therefore appears dark.

PAGE 140, LENS PROBLEM

a. If the rays came from the right, they would reflect from each glass surface back toward the right. No such reflections are observed. But there are reflections back toward the left; therefore the rays came from the left.

b. The three parallel rays at A reflect from the concave surface at H to focus at I.

c. The ray at J is formed by reflection of the top ray at glass surface K, followed by refraction at surface H.

d. The converging rays at E are caused by reflection at surface M, followed by refraction at surface N.

e. The ray at O is formed by reflection at surface N. It strikes the surface at L beyond the "critical angle" (see page 62), and is therefore completely reflected from the smooth glass surface at L.

154